Introduction to Management Science
Study Guide

Bernard W. Taylor

Constance H. McLaren
Indiana State University

Bruce J. McLaren
Indiana State University

wcb
Wm. C. Brown Company Publishers
Dubuque, Iowa

2-08063-02

Third Printing, 1983

Contents

Preface *v*

1 Management Science 1
Key Concepts 1
Quiz 1
Problems 2

2 Introduction to Linear Programming
Model Formation 5
Key Concepts 5
Quiz 5
Problems 6
Case: *Le Beau Croissants (A)* *8*

3 Graphical Illustration of Linear
Programming 9
Key Concepts 9
Quiz 9
Problems 11
Case: *Le Beau Croissants (B)* *13*

4 The Simplex Solution Method 15
Key Concepts 15
Quiz 15
Problems 16
Case: *Walters Fabricating Company (A)* *20*

5 The Minimization Problem and
Irregular Types of Linear Programming
Problems 21
Key Concepts 21
Quiz 21
Problems 22
Case: *JB Cartage Company* *25*

6 Postoptimality Analysis 27
Key Concepts 27
Quiz 27
Problems 28
Case: *Walters Fabricating Company (B)* *31*

7 Transportation and Assignment
Problems 33
Key Concepts 33
Quiz 34
Problems 35
Case: *Post County Public Library* *38*

8 Integer Programming 39
Key Concepts 39
Quiz 39
Problems 40
Case: *Massachusetts Metals* *43*

9 Goal Programming 45
Key Concepts 45
Quiz 45
Problems 46
Case: *Pan Global Airlines* *49*

10 Probability 51
Key Concepts 51
Quiz 52
Problems 53

11 Decision Analysis 57
Key Concepts 57
Quiz 58
Problems 59
Case: *The Golden Villa* *62*

12 Game Theory 63
Key Concepts 63
Quiz 63
Problems 64
Case: *Hammer-Scissors-Paper* *65*

13 Markov Analysis 67
Key Concepts 67
Quiz 67
Problems 68
Case: *Ross Associates* *70*

14 Queuing Analysis 71
Key Concepts 71
Quiz 73
Problems 73
Case: *Jordan Appliance Company* *76*

15 Simulation 77
Key Concepts 77
Quiz 78
Problems 78
Case: *Johnson Industries 81*

16 Forecasting 83
Key Concepts 83
Quiz 84
Problems 85
Case: *Davis Wood Stove 87*

17 Inventory Analysis with Certain
Demand 89
Key Concepts 89
Quiz 90
Problems 91
Case: *Fischer Nurseries, Inc. 95*

18 Inventory Analysis with Uncertain
Demand 97
Key Concepts 97
Quiz 98
Problems 99
Case: *Hamilton Distribution Company 101*

19 Network Flow Models 103
Key Concepts 103
Quiz 104
Problems 104
Case: *National Video Cable 107*

20 CPM and PERT Network Analysis
109
Key Concepts 109
Quiz 110
Problems 111
Case: *Lundell Construction 115*

21 Dynamic Programming 117
Key Concepts 117
Quiz 117
Problems 118
Case: *Griffin Electronics 121*

22 Break-Even Analysis 123
Key Concepts 123
Quiz 123
Problems 124

23 Problem Analysis with Calculus 125
Key Concepts 125
Quiz 125
Problems 125

24 Nonlinear Programming 129
Key Concepts 129
Quiz 129
Problems 130
Case: *Mrs. Worthington's Portfolio 131*

25 The Manager and Management
Science
Management Information Systems and
Implementation 133
Key Concepts 133

Appendix A 135
Appendix B 137
Solutions 139

Contents

Preface

In preparing this study guide, we have tried to keep in mind the variety of students who are enrolled in introductory management science classes and the diversity of their backgrounds. To this end, we feel that this study guide will be useful not only to the student who will benefit from additional examples and explanations, but also to the student who is intrigued by the material and would enjoy expanding the concepts learned in the text.

While this study guide has been designed to accompany and complement *Introduction to Management Science,* the problems, cases, and many chapter quizzes are general enough to be used in any management science course.

Chapters of the study guide follow those of the text. Each chapter begins with a chapter outline of key concepts. This is similar to the outline a student would prepare of the chapter and covers the important points of the chapter, with key terms highlighted.

Chapter quizzes reinforce the concepts. Questions vary among true-false, short answer, and exercise depending on the nature of the material.

There are at least two problems for each chapter, complete with step-by-step solutions. The problems can be used as additional examples before working problems in the text, or as supplementary, expanded problems with solutions so students can check their calculations.

In chapters where it is suitable, a case has been included. We have tried to make the cases realistic and challenging, yet keep them of a size that is practical for hand solution. There are several issues in each case, and we hope they will provoke thought beyond a simple numerical example.

Our thanks go to the Management-Finance Department of the School of Business at Indiana State University for its support and to Denise Davidson for preparation of the manuscript.

1 Management Science

Key Concepts

I. Management science
  A. *Management science* is defined as the application of mathematical techniques to management problems in order to help managers make better decisions.
  B. Management science can also be called the following.
    1. Operations research
    2. Quantitative methods
    3. Quantitative analysis
    4. Decision science
  C. Management science is an approach to problem solving often used by the government, the military, business and industry, and health care organizations.
II. Problem solving
  A. Management science encompasses a logical, systematic approach to problem solving.
  B. Solutions may be done by hand or on a computer.
  C. Problem solving entails the following steps.
    1. Observe the situation
    2. Define the problem
    3. Construct a model of the problem
    4. Solve the model
    5. Implement the results
III. Important terminology
  A. A *variable* is a symbol used in a model because no set numerical value has been specified for that item.
    1. The value of a *dependent variable* is determined from the numbers in the equation.
    2. The value of an *independent variable* is determined before it is placed in the equation and so is dependent upon nothing else in the equation.
  B. *Parameters* are numbers in the equation.
  C. The equation as a whole is known as a *functional relationship*.
  D. A profit or cost equation is known as the *objective function*.
  E. A resource equation is known as a *constraint*.
  F. A *decision variable* is a symbol whose value represents an action for the manager.

Quiz

True-False

T (F) 1. Management science has few applications aside from business production problems.

(T) F 2. The advent of the computer has greatly improved the popularity and practicality of management science applications.

T (F) 3. A management scientist is a person whose main function is to run the computer programs to solve management science problems.

(T) F 4. In order to define a management science problem, the goals and objectives of the firm and the limitations of the solution must also be considered.

T (F) 5. A management science symbol is a mathematical representation of an existing problem.

T (F)   6. Dependent and independent variables are both parameters of a management science model.

(T) F   7. Management science models consist of functional relationships and restrictions on those relationships.

T (F)   8. A constraint must be in the form of an equality.

T (F)   9. The solution to a management science model is always the decision the firm should make.

(T) F 10. Feedback from a management science model allows a manager to test varying conditions and decisions.

T (F) 11. Math programming refers to the writing of computer programs to solve mathematical models.

(T) F 12. In a deterministic model, you know with certainty what will happen.

(T) F 13. Management science is not only a science but also an art.

Short Answer

14. What is another name for operations research, quantitative methods, quantitative analysis, and decision sciences?   Mgt. Science

15. What are the steps in attacking a management science problem?
Observe, Define, Construct model, Solution, implement

Problems

1. The developer of a large apartment complex has purchased 600 square yards of vinyl flooring for the apartment kitchens. There are 100 apartments in the complex. Each kitchen requires 9 square yards of vinyl. The developer needs to know how many kitchen floors can be finished. Develop and solve a mathematical model for this problem situation.

Solution

Let x = the number of kitchens to be floored.
The objective is to cover as many kitchen floors as possible, or

maximize x

We need to be sure that the requirement for the availability of the vinyl is not violated. The relationship is

$9x \leq 600$

We also need to specify that no more than 100 kitchens need floors.

$x \leq 100$

The model should be:

maximize x
subject to
$\quad 9x \leq 600$
$\quad\ \ x \leq 100$

Using simple algebra, the first constraint tells us that x must be less than or equal to 66⅔. The second constraint doesn't restrict us at all since we have only enough vinyl to complete 66 kitchens.

2. Think about the problems facing a school corporation that has consolidated three small high schools into one large school and must plan new routes for the school buses. How could the management science approach be applied to solve this problem?

Solution

1. *Observe the situation.* The school corporation should recognize that students will need to travel new and different routes to arrive at the new school and that more buses may be necessary.

2. *Define the problem.* How many buses will be necessary to transport the students to school? Which students will ride which buses?

3. *Construct a model of the problem.*

4. *Solve the model.* Often, a management scientist is hired to model and solve a problem of this complexity. However, information on the number of students, where they live, and how many buses and drivers are available will be supplied to the management scientist by the school corporation.

5. *Implement the results.* Inform bus drivers of their routes and students of their bus schedules.

2 Introduction to Linear Programming
Model Formation

Key Concepts

I. The *linear programming* technique may be used to organize and assist in making managerial decisions by following the procedure below.
  A. Identify the decision or problem as being solvable by linear programming.
    1. Linear programming is applied to those problems with an objective to be accomplished subject to some restrictions.
      a) The objective is either to *maximize* a quantity such as profit, production, or rate of return or to *minimize* a quantity such as cost, time, or distance.
      b) The restrictions, or *constraints,* describe known relationships such as those between required and available resources, practical or contractual specifications, and supply and demand.
      c) Decision variables represent levels of activity by the firm, and their possible values indicate courses of action for the firm.
    2. Both the objective (stated as a function of the decision variables) and the constraints (mathematical equations or inequalities) must be linear (no products of decision variables).
  B. Use the facts of the problem to build a mathematical model.
    1. Be sure that the units on either side of each constraint are the same and that terms of the objective function are all in dollars or hours, or whatever is appropriate.
    2. Add constraints requiring each decision variable to be nonnegative.
  C. Solve the mathematical model, using a programmed series of steps (the subject of later chapters), to obtain the best decision for the firm.
    1. Those sets of values for the decision variables that do not violate any of the constraints are called feasible solutions to the problem.
    2. The solution to the problem will be the set of values of the decision variables that best accomplishes the objective.
II. Some areas of application of linear programming are product mix problems, investment problems, marketing problems, transportation problems, and scheduling problems.

Quiz

Short Answer

1. Which of the following objective functions are permissible in a linear programming problem?
    a) maximize $Z = 3x_1 + 2x_2 + x_3$
    b) maximize $Z = 3x_1 - 2x_2 - x_3$
    c) minimize $Z = x_1 + x_2$
    d. maximize $Z = 3x_1^2 + 2x_2$ — NON-LINEAR
    e. maximize $Z = x_1 + 2x_1x_2 + 4x_2$ NON-LINEAR
    f) minimize $Z = x_1 + 2$
    g) minimize $Z = -x_1 - 2x_2$
    h. maximize $Z = 3\sqrt{x_1 + 4x_2 - x_3}$ — NON-LINEAR

5

2. Which of the following constraints are permissible in a linear programming problem?
   a. $3x_1 + 4x_2 \leq 12$
   b. $2x_1^2 - 3 \leq 15$
   c. $x_1 + x_2 \geq 100$
   d. $x_1 + x_2 \geq x_3$
   e. $-12x_1 - 4 \leq 0$
   f. $x_1 = x_2$
   g. $4x_1 + x_1 x_2 \leq 25$
   h. $(x_1 + x_2) \div x_3 \leq 3$

3. Let x_1 = the number of units of product A produced
      x_2 = the number of units of product B produced
   Write the appropriate linear programming constraint(s) for each of the following situations.
   a. It takes 5 hours to make one unit of product A and 3 hours to make one unit of product B. The firm has 300 hours available.
   b. Each unit of product A requires 4 pounds of calcium and 2 pounds of sand. Each unit of product B requires 8 pounds of calcium and no sand. The firm has 500 pounds of calcium available and 800 pounds of sand.
   c. The firm can sell no more than a total of 75 products.
   d. The number of product A items must be no larger than twice the number of product B items.

4. Given the following linear programming problem, identify the possible solutions that are feasible and the solutions that are infeasible. Explain why those are infeasible.

   maximize $Z = 10x_1 + 12x_2$
   subject to
   $$3x_1 + 4x_2 \leq 24$$
   $$x_1 + x_2 \leq 7$$
   $$2x_1 - x_2 \leq 0$$
   $$x_1, x_2 \geq 0$$

   a. $x_1 = 8, x_2 = 6$
   b. $x_1 = 2, x_2 = 5$
   c. $x_1 = 1, x_2 = 2$
   d. $x_1 = 0, x_2 = 7$
   e. $x_1 = 5, x_2 = 2$
   f. $x_1 = 4, x_2 = 3$

Problems

1. The Industrial Products Division of MCI Corporation blends chemical substances to form industrial cleaners. Regular and super strength cleaners are made. Each container of regular cleaner uses 2 pounds of chemical XA and 3 pounds of XJ. Super strength cleaner requires 5 pounds of chemical XA but only 2 pounds of XJ. Inventory records show that the division has on hand 1,000 pounds of XA and 800 pounds of XJ. If the profit per container of regular is $20 and of super strength is $25, show a linear programming formulation of this problem whose solution would indicate how many containers of each cleaner should be produced.

Solution

The division wants to know how many containers of each cleaner should be produced, so the decision variables would be:

x_1 = the number of containers of regular cleaner to be made
x_2 = the number of containers of super strength cleaner to be made

The objective is to maximize profit, so the objective function would be:

maximize $Z = 20x_1 + 25x_2$

The constraints deal with the amount of chemical on hand. We must balance our requirements and uses of the chemical with the amount available.

For XA, $2x_1 + 5x_2 \leq 1,000$
For XJ, $3x_1 + 2x_2 \leq 800$

Notice that the unit on both sides of the first inequality is pounds of XA and on both sides of the second inequality is pounds of XJ.

The final model would then be:

maximize $Z = 20x_1 + 25x_2$
subject to
$$2x_1 + 5x_2 \leq 1,000$$
$$3x_1 + 2x_2 \leq 800$$
$$x_1, x_2 \geq 0$$

2. The Investment Group recommends to its clients those securities, bond issues, and real estate offerings considered to have a positive potential for high return. For Ellen Lawson, a new client, two possible investments have been recommended. The first is to buy stock in Peripherals, Inc., a computer company. The second is to buy shares in H.O.U.S.E., a real estate group that is buying, renovating, and renting older homes. Each share of Peripherals stock is currently selling for $75. Shares for H.O.U.S.E. sell for $50 each. Ellen has $10,000 to invest and feels that the investment in the computer stock should be no larger than $6,000. The real estate group will not allow any one investor to own more than 100 shares of H.O.U.S.E. If the estimated return for a share of Peripherals stock one year from now is $12 and a share of the real estate group is $8, how should Ellen's $10,000 be allocated to maximize return a year from now? Develop a linear programming model whose solution would indicate the best investment.

Solution

We need to know how many shares of each investment should be purchased, so the decision variables would be:

$x_1 =$ the number of shares of Peripherals, Inc., to be purchased
$x_2 =$ the number of shares of H.O.U.S.E. to be purchased

The objective is to maximize total return, which is given by the sum of return per share multiplied by number of shares for each investment.

maximize $Z = 12x_1 + 8x_2$

The constraints deal with the total investment possible and restrictions on the amount of each investment Ellen is able to purchase.

$$75x_1 + 50x_2 \leq 10,000$$
$$75x_1 \leq 6,000$$
$$x_2 \leq 100$$

Notice that the first two constraints are in dollars and the third is in number of shares.
The final model would then be:

maximize $Z = 12x_1 + 8x_2$
subject to
$$75x_1 + 50x_2 \leq 10,000$$
$$75x_1 \leq 6,000$$
$$x_2 \leq 100$$
$$x_1, x_2 \geq 0$$

Upon returning home after a visit to his father's birthplace in France, Philippe Le Beau was enthusiastically contemplating a venture that he thought would result in great success and profit. While walking through the streets of Paris, Le Beau had seen, interspersed with American fast-food chains, the beginning French inroads into the industry. Those delicious French pastries, croissants, were being prepared, frozen, shipped out to chains of shops, warmed and purchased by great numbers of hungry Parisians who were glad to trade freshness for convenience. Le Beau reasoned that Americans were attracted to the fast-food concept, had readily adopted tacos, fish and chips, and pizza in addition to their native hamburgers, and therefore should also readily develop a taste for his import.

At 32, Philippe Le Beau had worked as an accountant for a medium-sized CPA firm since his graduation from college ten years earlier. He had passed the CPA exam a year after graduation and his responsibilities had regularly increased as his experience had grown. As a person who always needed many challenges, he was looking for a project that could be done, at least in the initial stages, on the side. As he explained to his old friend, real estate broker Wally Ring, "I'm going to start small, with one shop. I want you to find me a small property, with room for parking, in a middle- to upper-middle-class shopping/business area. If it flies after six months, then we'll talk expansion. One of our exsecretaries is going to be the supervisor, and I'll hire college kids for the counter. I'll do all the cooking and freezing on Saturdays for the coming week."

"Well, Philippe," Wally began, "I can think of a couple of places that would be suitable. If you're serious about this venture, knowing as well as you do the likelihood of failure for small businesses, then I'd say we can have you set up in, say, two weeks? Of course, you'd have to redecorate, but that shouldn't be too much of a problem. If you don't mind my asking, are you swinging this by yourself, or will a bank be involved?"

Philippe hesitated a moment, then answered, "I'm going alone on this one. From my financial situation, it will work out better, but, remember, I *am* starting small."

"Okay. If anybody can do it, you probably can," Wally reassured his friend. "By the way, Kate and I watched a report on these French croissant shops the other night on NBC news. The food really did look good! I'll get back to you when we're ready to go see some properties."

As he waited for word on a property, Philippe gathered information on equipment, licenses, food vendors, customary restaurant practices, and costs. He knew there were many decisions to be made, so he organized his information and preliminary findings into a series of documents (see exhibit 2.1).

By the time Wally returned his call a week later with word of three properties to view, Philippe had accomplished all hiring, legal work, and planning. There was only one remaining question to be answered. How many of each croissant should be prepared?

Exhibit 2.1 Proposed Menu and Preparation Details

Croissants are envelopes or crescents of flaky rich pastry, which may or may not be filled with a mixture of ingredients before baking. Philippe planned to offer these varieties:

1. Chicken-Cheese-Mushroom Croissants (named "Le Plus")
   Ingredients: Pastry—6 ounces
   Chicken—4 ounces
   Cheese—3 ounces
   Mushrooms—2 ounces
   Time to assemble: 1 minute
   Profit $1.00
2. Pepperoni-Cheese-Mushroom Croissants (named "La Mediterranee")
   Ingredients: Pastry—6 ounces
   Pepperoni—3 ounces
   Cheese—5 ounces
   Mushrooms—2 ounces
   Time to assemble: 45 seconds
   Profit $1.25
3. Fruit-Cheese-Dessert Croissants (named "La Parisienne")
   Ingredients: Pastry—4 ounces
   Cheese—2 ounces
   Apples—2 ounces
   Time to assemble: 30 seconds
   Profit $.80

The following considerations must be made:

1. Mushrooms are available from a produce vendor in a crate of 50 pounds per week.
2. Cheese deliveries are made in amounts of 75 pounds per week.
3. Pastry will be made in batches totaling 400 pounds per week.
4. There are no restrictions on the amounts of chicken, pepperoni, or apples available per week.
5. After allocating cooking time, there will be 10 work hours available for assembly time and 2 work hours available for packaging. It will take 5 seconds to package each croissant for the freezer.

Introduction to Linear Programming

3 Graphical Illustration of Linear Programming

Key Concepts

I. Linear programming problems with only two decision variables can be readily solved *graphically*.

II. The first step is to plot the constraints on the graph to find the *feasible region,* those points that satisfy all of the constraints.

    A. First, plot the line of each constraint by finding two points that satisfy the constraint expressed as an equation, and then connect those two points with a straight line.

    B. Then, determine the area adjacent to the constraint that satisfies the constraint as an inequality.

    C. The feasible region is determined by the intersection, or overlap, of the areas determined by all the constraints.

III. The second step is to locate the point that will accomplish the objective of the problem.

    A. Arbitrarily select a value for the objective function and plot the resulting line on the graph.

    B. Slide this line (always remaining parallel) in the direction of improving the objective function until it intersects the feasible region in only one point (or line segment), the optimal solution.

    C. The optimal solution is always on the boundary of the feasible region.

IV. The third step is to solve for the coordinates of the optimal solution.

    A. Determine the two constraint lines that intersect in the point for the optimal solution.

    B. Solve these two equations simultaneously to find the coordinates of the optimal solution.

    C. To find the value of the objective function, substitute the values for the decision variables into the objective function.

V. An alternative procedure can be used for the second and third steps.

    A. Find the coordinates of all of the extreme points of the feasible region by solving pairs of simultaneous equations.

    B. Substitute the coordinates of the extreme points (*feasible solutions*) into the objective function to see which point best accomplishes the objective (*optimal solution*).

Quiz

True-False

T (F)   1. The solution to any linear programming problem can be found graphically.

(T) F   2. The feasible region is shown on the graph as the area in which all of the areas determined by the constraints overlap.

T (F)   3. The optimal solution will always be exactly one point.

(T) F   4. The optimal solution will never be in the interior of the feasible region.

T (F)   5. The constraint $x_1 + x_2 \leq 5$, when graphed as a line segment, passes through the point $x_1 = 5$, $x_2 = 5$.

(T) F   6. The constraint $2x_1 + 3x_2 \leq 6$, when graphed as a line segment, passes through the points $x_1 = 3$, $x_2 = 0$ and $x_1 = 0$, $x_2 = 2$.

Exercises

7. Solve the following equations simultaneously.

$$2x_1 + 5x_2 = 10$$
$$x_1 + 2x_2 = 4$$

$$0x_1 + x_2 = 2$$
$$x_1 = 0$$
$$x_2 = 2$$

8. Solve the following equations simultaneously.

$$x_1 + x_2 = 12$$
$$2x_1 - 3x_2 = 10$$

9. Solve the following equations simultaneously.

$$2x_1 + 4x_2 = 12$$
$$-x_1 + x_2 = 0$$

Given the following linear programming problem and its graph of constraint lines, answer questions 10–15.

maximize $Z = x_1 + x_2$
subject to
1) $10x_1 + 8x_2 \le 80$
2) $x_1 + 2x_2 \le 12$
3) $x_1 \le 7$
4) $x_2 \le 5$
$x_1, x_2 \ge 0$

Figure 3.1 Graph for questions 10–15.

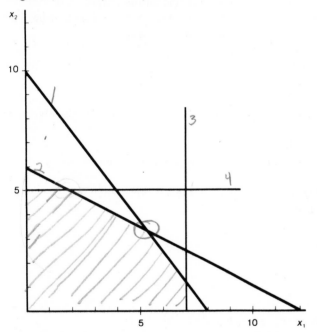

10. Place the numbers 1, 2, 3, and 4 on the appropriate constraints.

11. Shade the feasible region for the problem.

12. By sliding the objective function line in the direction of increasing the value of the objective function, find the optimal solution.

13. Determine which constraints intersect to form the optimal solution point. Solve these equations simultaneously to find the coordinates of the optimal solution.

14. If the objective function is maximize $Z = 3x_1 + 3x_2$, what is the optimal solution?

15. If the objective function is maximize $Z = x_1 + 2x_2$, what is the optimal solution?

Graphical Illustration of Linear Programming

Problems

1. Solve the following linear programming problem graphically.

$$\text{maximize } Z = 6x_1 + 10x_2$$

subject to

$$x_1 + 2x_2 \leq 20 \quad \text{①}$$
$$4x_1 + 3x_2 \leq 48 \quad \text{②}$$
$$x_1, x_2 \geq 0$$

Solution

First, determine two points that satisfy each constraint when expressed as an equation. Since x_1 and x_2 must both be greater than or equal to zero, it is convenient to let $x_2 = 0$ and solve for x_1 in an equation, and then let $x_1 = 0$ and solve for x_2. This procedure determines two points for each constraint and allows you to draw the line.

Constraint Line	When $x_2 = 0$	When $x_1 = 0$
$x_1 + 2x_2 = 20$	$x_1 = 20, x_2 = 0$	$x_1 = 0, x_2 = 10$
$4x_1 + 3x_2 = 48$	$x_1 = 12, x_2 = 0$	$x_1 = 0, x_2 = 16$

Figure 3.2 Graph of model constraints and feasible region.

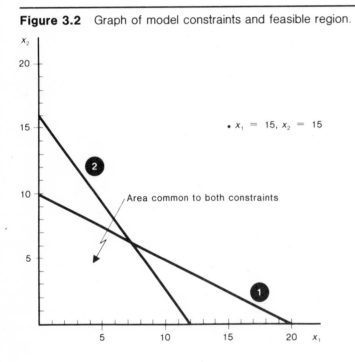

To locate the feasible region, we notice that, for example, $x_1 = 0$, $x_2 = 0$ satisfies constraint 1 and $x_1 = 15$, $x_2 = 15$ does not, so the area that satisfies constraint 1 must be "below" the constraint. Similar reasoning will indicate that the area satisfying constraint 2 must be "below" that constraint. The intersection of these areas is the feasible region.

Figure 3.3 Objective function lines for $Z = 30$ and for optimal solution.

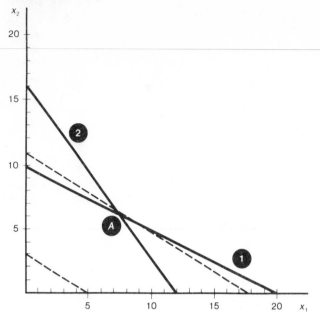

To locate the point on the graph that will maximize the objective function, let us arbitrarily let $Z = 30$. We then can graph the line $6x_1 + 10x_2 = 30$. We notice that, by sliding this line out, we are increasing the value of Z, which is our objective. Finally, we see that the objective function line intersects the feasible region in only one point, point A on the graph. Point A is formed by the intersection of constraints 1 and 2, so we must solve these equations simultaneously in order to find the coordinates of A.

$$x_1 + 2x_2 = 20 \quad ①$$
$$4x_1 + 3x_2 = 48 \quad ②$$

Solving equation 1 for x_1 and substituting $x_1 = 20 - 2x_2$ into equation 2 , we have:

$$4(20 - 2x_2) + 3x_2 = 48$$
$$80 - 8x_2 + 3x_2 = 48$$
$$80 - 5x_2 = 48$$
$$- 5x_2 = -32$$
$$x_2 = 6.4$$

Substituting $x_2 = 6.4$ into either equation, we find:

$$x_1 + 2(6.4) = 20$$
$$x_1 + 12.8 = 20$$
$$x_1 = 7.2$$

The optimal solution to this problem is:

$$x_1 = 7.2, x_2 = 6.4$$

and the value of the objective function is:

$$Z = 6(7.2) + 10(6.4) = 107.2$$

2. Solve the following linear programming problem graphically.

   minimize $Z = 2x_1 + 3x_2$
   subject to
   $$x_1 + x_2 \geq 6$$
   $$4x_1 + 2x_2 \geq 16$$
   $$x_1, x_2 \geq 0$$

Graphical Illustration of Linear Programming

Solution

The constraint lines and feasible region are shown in figure 3.4. Notice that because these constraints are all $\geq$, the feasible region is not bounded on all sides.

Figure 3.4 Feasible region and objective function lines for $Z = 18$ and optimal solution.

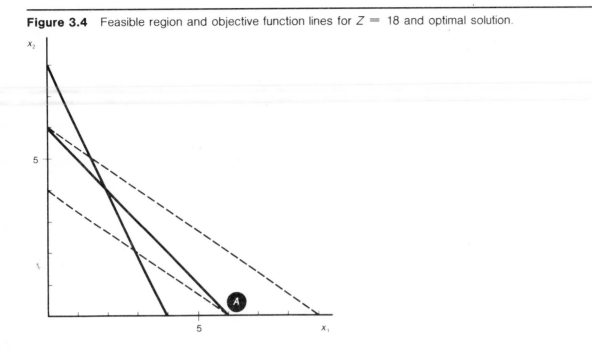

Arbitrarily letting $Z = 18$, we see that to improve the objective function, the line must slide in toward the origin. The last point it intersects is point A. We see that point A is the one determined by $x_1 + x_2 = 6$ and $x_2 = 0$.

Solving these two equations simultaneously, we find the optimal solution to be $x_1 = 6$, $x_2 = 0$, and $Z = 2(6) + 3(0) = 12$.

Case *Le Beau Croissants (B)*

Le Beau Croissants had been operating for nearly a month after opening its small shop in a shopping complex that serviced several office buildings. Philippe Le Beau was gratified with the success of his venture, but realized there was room for improvement. As he said to his friends Wally and Kate Ring one evening, "I'm thinking of making some changes. The Mediterranee just isn't selling like I'd thought it would. I suppose it's too close to pizza, and people would rather eat pizza for that taste. I think I'm going to pull it off the menu."

"I liked it," said Kate, "but maybe you're right. How are the sales of the others going?"

"Very well, thanks. In fact, too well. I've run out of the dessert croissant all three weeks, while having extra of Le Plus. Since I don't really like to freeze them for very long, I'm having a problem knowing how many of each to make."

"Do you have any ideas about how many people order both Le Plus and La Parisienne?" Kate asked. "If you could figure out some kind of ratio, then we could make that fact a constraint in your problem and you could find the optimal mix."

"Kate, that's a great idea. I'll ask my employees to be a little more observant about the customers' preferences, and then build that into the model," Philippe said, relieved that there was going to be a solution to his problem.

A week later, Philippe was facing a note written by the croissant shop supervisor. The Mediterranee croissant had been removed from the menu with few complaints. There were two sentences in the note that Philippe knew would be the key to the proper weekly production levels. The note read:

About 80% of the people who order Le Plus also order La Parisienne. In addition, about half of the customers come only for dessert, so we could sell that many more of La Parisienne.

Philippe knew that if he could build these facts into his original linear programming problem he would be able to solve the problem graphically, since there were now only two kinds of croissants in production. How many of each croissant should he make each week?

Graphical Illustration of Linear Programming

4 The Simplex Solution Method

Key Concepts

I. The *simplex solution procedure* is a general technique for solving linear programming problems with any number of decision variables.
   A. The problem is put into a table form and then mathematical steps are performed on this table.
   B. The simplex method presents successive solution points of the problem, each better than the previous, until the optimal solution is found.

II. A specific series of steps must be followed to use the simplex algorithm.
   A. The constraints must be converted from inequalities to equalities by the addition of a unique *slack variable*, which represents amount of unused resource, to every inequality.
   B. The problem is then put into the tableau form.
      1. The first solution is obtained by letting all of the decision variables equal zero, and letting the slack variables be the basic variables.
      2. The constraints are inserted into the table along with the values of the slack variables and the c_j values.
      3. The z_j values are found by multiplying each c_j column value by each variable column value and then summing.
      4. The $c_j - z_j$ values are found by subtracting the z_j row values from the c_j row values.
   C. To find the next better solution, a *nonbasic* variable will become *basic*, replacing a current basic variable.
      1. The variable that enters the basis (becomes positive) will be the one with the *highest positive value* of $c_j - z_j$, or *net increase* per unit of entering nonbasic variable.
      2. The variable that leaves the basis (becomes zero) will be the one with the *minimum non-negative quotient* of the "quantity" values to the pivot column values.
   D. Simplex operations are used to calculate the row values in the next tableau.
      1. New pivot row values are obtained by dividing the old pivot row values by the pivot number.
      2. New tableau row values are obtained by subtracting, from the old tableau row values, the product of the corresponding coefficient in the pivot column and the corresponding new tableau pivot row values.
   E. The *optimal solution* has been found when, after any iteration, all values in the $c_j - z_j$ row are negative or zero.

Quiz

True-False

T ⓕ 1. A linear programming problem with two decision variables and four constraints will have a solution with two variables with positive values.

ⓣ F 2. Any linear programming problem can be solved by the simplex algorithm.

ⓣ F 3. Every basic feasible solution that appears in a simplex tableau of a problem with only two variables will also be an extreme point of that problem's graphical solution.

ⓣ F 4. The z_j row of the simplex tableau measures how much profit will be given up by discontinuing the production of one of the items.

T ⓕ 5. The simplex procedure has found the optimal solution to the problem when all the entries in the $c_j - z_j$ row are ≥ 0.

Exercises

6. Develop the initial simplex tableau for the linear programming problem below by completing the table.

maximize $Z = 10x_1 + 12x_2$
subject to
$$x_1 + x_2 \le 5$$
$$2x_1 + 3x_2 \le 8$$
$$4x_1 + x_2 \le 15$$
$$x_1, x_2 \ge 0$$

c_i	basic variables	quantity	10 x_1	12 x_2	0 s_1	0 s_2	0 s_3
0	S_1	5	1	1	1	0	0
0	S_2	8	2	3	0	1	0
0	S_3	15	4	1	0	0	1
	z_i	0	0	0	0	0	0
	$c_i - z_i$		10	12	0	0	0

Use the following simplex tableau to answer questions 7–10.

c_i	basic variables	quantity	3 x_1	7 x_2	5 x_3	0 s_1	0 s_2
7	x_2	5	1/2	1	1/4	1/2	0
0	s_2	20	2	0	3/4	-1/2	1
	z_i		7/2	7	7/4	7/2	0
	$c_i - z_i$		-1/2	0	13/4	-7/2	0

7. Complete the blanks in this tableau.

8. How many decision variables and constraints were in the original problem?   3 & 2

9. What is the current solution? Give values for all variables. Is it optimal?   0, 5, 0, 0, 20   35   NO

10. If the current solution is not optimal, indicate which variable would enter the basis and which one would leave to construct the new tableau. x_3 , s_2

Problems

1. Use the simplex procedure to solve the following problem, which was solved graphically in chapter 3. Compare the solutions at each tableau with the extreme points on your graph.

maximize $Z = 6x_1 + 10x_2$
subject to
$$x_1 + 2x_2 \le 20$$
$$4x_1 + 3x_2 \le 48$$
$$x_1, x_2 \ge 0$$

The Simplex Solution Method

Solution

The initial tableau is written with slack variables having been added to each constraint.

Table 4.1 The Initial Simplex Tableau

c_j			8	10	0	0
	basic variables	quantity	x_1	x_2	s_1	s_2
0 ⟶	s_1	20	1	2	1	0
0	s_2	48	4	3	0	1
	z_j	0	0	0	0	0
	$c_j - z_j$		6	10	0	0

Since the largest element in the $c_j - z_j$ row is 10, x_2 will enter the basis. Since the minimum of the ratios of the quantity column to the x_2 column is $20/2 = 10$, s_1 will leave the basis. The pivot row is shown by an arrow and the pivot element is shaded in table 4.1. The initial solution is $x_1 = 0$ and $x_2 = 0$.

The new tableau pivot row values are computed by dividing through all of the old pivot row values by 2, to make the pivot element a 1. These values are listed in table 4.2. The second row is computed as shown in table 4.2 by subtracting 3 times the new pivot row from the old second row.

Table 4.2 Computation of the x_2 Row for the Second Simplex Tableau

Column	Old Row Value	− Corresponding Coefficient in Pivot Column	× New Tableau Pivot Row Value	= New Tableau Row Value
quantity	48	− (3	× 10)	= 18
x_1	4	− (3	× 1/2)	= 5/2
x_2	3	− (3	× 1)	= 0
s_1	0	− (3	× 1/2)	= −3/2
s_2	1	− (3	× 0)	= 1

The second simplex tableau is shown in table 4.3. The current solution is $x_1 = 0$ and $x_2 = 10$.

Table 4.3 The Second Simplex Tableau

c_j			6	10	0	0
	basic variables	quantity	x_1	x_2	s_1	s_2
10	x_2	10	1/2	1	1/2	0
0 ⟶	s_2	18	5/2	0	−3/2	1
	z_j	100	5	10	5	0
	$c_j - z_j$		1	0	−5	0

Because there is still a positive number in the $c_j - z_j$ row, another iteration is necessary. The variable x_1 will enter the basis, and s_2 will leave (minimum ratio is $18 \div 5/2 = 36/5$). The pivot row is shown by an arrow and the pivot element is shaded in table 4.3.

The new tableau pivot row values are computed by dividing through all of the old pivot row values by 5/2. The new x_1 row is then found by subtracting 1/2 times the new pivot row from the old first row.

Table 4.4 Computation of the x_1 Row for the Third Simplex Tableau

Column	Old Row Value	—	Corresponding Coefficient in Pivot Column	×	New Tableau Pivot Row Value	=	New Tableau Row Value
quantity	10	—	(1/2	×	36/5)	=	32/5
x_1	1/2	—	(1/2	×	1)	=	0
x_2	1	—	(1/2	×	0)	=	1
s_1	1/2	—	(1/2	×	−3/5)	=	4/5
s_2	0	—	(1/2	×	2/5)	=	−1/5

The third simplex tableau is shown in table 4.5.

Table 4.5 The Third Simplex Tableau

c_j			6	10	0	0
	basic variables	quantity	x_1	x_2	s_1	s_2
10	x_2	32/5	0	1	4/5	−1/5
6	x_1	36/5	1	0	−3/5	2/5
	z_j	536/5	6	10	22/5	2/5
	$c_j - z_j$		0	0	−22/5	−2/5

The optimal solution has been found since there are no longer any positive entries in the $c_j - z_j$ row. The optimal solution is $x_1 = 36/5$, $x_2 = 32/5$, and $Z = 536/5$. The slack variables, s_1 and s_2, are both equal to zero since they are not in the basis.

2. Use the simplex procedure to solve the following linear programming problem.

$$\text{maximize } Z = x_1 + 2x_2 + 4x_3$$
$$\text{subject to}$$
$$2x_1 + x_2 + 3x_3 \le 12$$
$$4x_1 + x_2 + x_3 \le 6$$
$$x_1, x_2, x_3 \ge 0$$

Solution

First, put in slack variables to make each constraint an equality. The initial tableau is shown in table 4.6.

Table 4.6 The Initial Simplex Tableau

c_j			1	2	4	0	0
	basic variables	quantity	x_1	x_2	x_3	s_1	s_2
0	s_1	12	2	1	3	1	0
0	s_2	6	4	1	1	0	1
	z_j	0	0	0	0	0	0
	$c_j - z_j$		1	2	4	0	0

The pivot element is the shaded 3, because the largest value in the $c_j - z_j$ row is the 4 in the x_3 column and the minimum ratio is the 12/3 in the s_1 row. As you develop more expertise with the simplex method, you will not need tables such as 4.2 and 4.4, so they are not included here. The second tableau is shown in table 4.7.

The Simplex Solution Method

Table 4.7 The Second Simplex Tableau

c_j	basic variables	quantity	1	2	4	0	0
			x_1	x_2	x_3	s_1	s_2
4	x_3	4	2/3	1/3	1	1/3	0
0	s_2	2	10/3	2/3	0	-1/3	1
	z_j	16	8/3	4/3	4	4/3	0
	c_j-z_j		-5/3	2/3	0	-4/3	0

Another iteration is necessary. The 2/3 in the x_2 column of the c_j-z_j row indicates that x_2 will enter the basis. The minimum ratio is $2 \div 2/3$ or 3, so s_2 will leave the basis. The new pivot row will be the old pivot row divided by 2/3. The new x_3 row will be the old x_3 row minus 1/3 of the new pivot row. The third tableau is shown in table 4.8.

Table 4.8 The Third Simplex Tableau

c_j	basic variables	quantity	1	2	4	0	0
			x_1	x_2	x_3	s_1	s_2
4	x_3	3	-1	0	1	1/2	-1/2
2	x_2	3	5	1	0	-1/2	3/2
	z_j	18	6	2	4	1	1
	c_j-z_j		-5	0	0	-1	-1

The optimal solution has been found since there are no longer any positive values in the c_j-z_j row. The solution is:

$$x_1 = 0 \qquad s_1 = 0$$
$$x_2 = 3 \qquad s_2 = 0$$
$$x_3 = 3 \qquad Z = 18$$

Special Hints for Simplex

It is very easy to make arithmetic mistakes when going from one tableau to the next. However, there are ways you can check your work.

1. Keep the numbers as fractions as long as you reasonably can before changing to decimals. This will prevent round off errors.

2. Every tableau should yield a solution that is feasible for the original linear programming problem.

3. Each variable in the basis will have as its column in the tableau a 1 in the row that lists that same variable in the basic variables column, the c_j value for that variable in the z_j row, and zeroes every place else.

4. The values in the quantity column may never be negative. If they are, review your calculations for that row. The pattern should always be (old tableau row) minus (corresponding element in pivot column) times (new tableau pivot row values).

5. The quantity of z_j, the value of the objective function, should improve with each tableau.

Many computer packages have been developed that solve linear programming problems by the simplex procedure. If your instructor makes one available to you after you have learned to perform simplex operations, use it to compare the solution and intermediate steps to what you have done by hand.

Appendix A shows an example of a linear programming problem solved by a computer package. This package is the Multi-Purpose Optimization System, developed at Northwestern University. The example problem is problem 2.

The Walters Fabricating Company, founded in 1910, had been making small metal items exclusively for industry when one day it was approached by Jane Kendrick, the purchasing agent for City University, a large, local, private school. Expansion into new classroom buildings and dormitories was necessitating new purchases for the university's maintenance staff.

"It's not very academic," Kendrick began her conversation with David Walters, sales manager of the firm, "but what we really need from you is wastebaskets, large trashcans, and metal dustpans. Our original supplier had a fire in his plant and can't meet the contract. We'll have four hundred students moving into the new dorm and a full schedule of classes in University Hall a week from now. Can you help?"

"I'm sure we can," Walters replied, "but to what extent, I'm not sure. Do you need it all from us?"

"No," Kendrick answered. "While it would simplify things, right now I'm just concerned about equipping the buildings. If you can tell me right away what you can provide, I'll go to Jones in Chicago for the remainder."

"I can have it for you by this afternoon if you'll just answer a few questions first. What is the maximum number of each of the three products?" Walters asked.

"That's easy. Five hundred wastebaskets, two hundred large trashcans, and two hundred dustpans," Kendrick rattled off the figures. "I'll look forward to hearing from you this afternoon."

David Walters's first visit was to the production manager who supplied him with a chart of production requirements for the three products. The chart is reproduced in exhibit 4.1. Next, Walters called the personnel manager and asked for any available labor hours in each of the four departments for the coming week. The answer is shown in exhibit 4.2. His final task was to ascertain the profit margin on each product. A quick visit with the accountants provided that information, shown in exhibit 4.3.

Exhibit 4.1   Time (in hours) Required for Production of Each Item

	Wastebaskets	Trashcans	Dustpans
Layout	.1	.2	.3
Cutting	.2	.4	.32
Welding	.2	.3	.2
Finishing	.3	.5	.2

Exhibit 4.2   Labor Hours Available in Each Department Week of August 19

Department	Total Hours
Layout	40
Cutting	20
Welding	30
Finishing	15

Exhibit 4.3   Profit Per Item

Item	Profit
Wastebasket	$2.50
Trashcan	$5.00
Dustpan	$3.00

As he sat down to evaluate the information, Walters was at first dismayed, thinking he would have to solve a linear programming problem with three decision variables and seven constraints. However, it soon dawned on him that practical considerations made three constraints redundant, so the problem was not as large as he had feared. "I might even have the answer back to the University *before* lunch," he said to himself as he sat down to work.

The Simplex Solution Method

5 The Minimization Problem and Irregular Types of Linear Programming Problems

Key Concepts

I. To solve linear programming problems with minimization objective functions and/or $\geq$ constraints, several adjustments must be made.
  - A. Constraints in the form of $\geq$ are converted to equalities by subtracting the *surplus* amount, s, from the left side.
  - B. To get an initial solution to the problem, an *artificial variable* is added to the constraint. Since it is added to one side of an equality and not the other, it has no meaning and we want its value to be zero in the final solution.
  - C. The cost of a surplus variable is $0; the cost of an artificial variable is M, a very large positive number that will prevent the artificial from having a nonzero value.
  - D. Since our objective is the opposite of what it was in a maximization problem, we will compute $z_j - c_j$ in the bottom row of the simplex tableau instead of $c_j - z_j$.
  - E. The simplex operations proceed as usual from this point, with the exception that once an *artificial* variable has left the basis, it will never return, so it may be dropped from future tableaus.

II. Problems with mixed constraints are handled by looking at the objective function and each constraint individually.
  - A. A different artificial variable must be added to each equality constraint. In maximization problems its c_j will be $-M$.
  - B. Inequality constraints are handled as before, as is the objective function.

III. Irregular types of linear programming problems are recognizable by indicators in the final tableau.
  - A. *Another optimal solution* exists if there is a zero in the $c_j - z_j$ (or $z_j - c_j$) row in the column of a nonbasic variable. This means that the variable could enter the basis, creating a different solution, with no net change in the value of the objective function.
  - B. The problem is *infeasible* (has no solution) if there is still an artificial variable in the basis when the $c_j - z_j$ (or $z_j - c_j$) row indicates the solution is optimal.
  - C. The problem is *unbounded* if there is no pivot element (or leaving basic variable) because all the elements in the chosen column are negative or zero, preventing the calculation of ratios.
  - D. *Ties* between the highest $c_j - z_j$ (or $z_j - c_j$) row values, or between two equal lowest ratios to locate the pivot element, should be broken arbitrarily.
  - E. A constraint formulated with a *negative quantity value* on the right side should be multiplied by negative one (which also reverses the sense of the inequality) to obtain a positive quantity value.

Quiz

Short Answer

1. When should an artificial variable be put into a constraint? $=$, $\geq$
2. What is the purpose of the artificial variables?   To get an initial solution
3. Why are slack variables added to constraints and surplus variables subtracted from constraints?
4. Explain the choice of M as the objective function coefficient of an artificial variable.   don't want them in final solution
5. Why are we able to eliminate artificial variables from tableaus once they leave the basis?   same
6. Explain why a problem with an artificial variable in the basis of the final iteration is infeasible.   have no meaning
7. Explain why, for minimization problems, we calculate $z_j - c_j$ instead of $c_j - z_j$.

8. Why does an "extra" zero in the $z_j - c_j$ (or $c_j - z_j$) row indicate an alternate optimal solution?

9. What factor in a tableau would indicate an unbounded solution, and why?

10. What is a degenerate solution?

Exercises

11. Do everything necessary to put this problem in the proper form for the initial simplex tableau.

   maximize $Z = 2x_1 + x_2 + 4x_3$
   subject to
   $$x_1 + x_2 + x_3 \geq 12$$
   $$x_1 - x_2 \geq -1$$
   $$2x_1 + 3x_2 - 2x_3 = 30$$
   $$x_1, x_2, x_3 \geq 0$$

   $Z = 2x_1 + x_2 + 4x_3 + 0s_1 + 0s_2 - MA_1 - MA_2$

   $x_1 + x_2 + x_3 - s_1 + A_1 = 12$

   $-x_1 + x_2 + s_2 = 1$

   $2x_1 + 3x_2 - 2x_3 + A_2 = 30$

12. Do everything necessary to this problem to put it in the proper form for the initial simplex tableau.

   minimize $Z = x_1 + 6x_2 + 3x_3 + x_4$
   subject to
   $$x_1 + x_2 + x_3 + x_4 \geq 50$$
   $$2x_1 + .5x_2 + x_3 + 1.5x_4 \geq 100$$
   $$x_1 - x_3 = 0$$
   $$x_1, x_2, x_3, x_4 \geq 0$$

   MIN $Z = x_1 + 6x_2 + 3x_3 + x_4 + 0s_1 + 0s_2 + A_1 + A_2 + A_3$

   $x_1 + x_2 + x_3 + x_4 - s_1 + A_1 = 50$

   $2x_1 + .5x_2 + x_3 + 1.5x_4 - s_2 + A_2 = 100$

   $x_1 - x_3 + A_3 = 0$

   $x_1, x_2, x_3, x_4, s_1, s_2, A_1, A_2 \geq 0$

Problems

1. The following problem was solved graphically in chapter 3. Now solve it by using the simplex algorithm, comparing the intermediate solutions to the points in your graph.

   minimize $Z = 2x_1 + 3x_2$
   subject to
   $$x_1 + x_2 \geq 6$$
   $$4x_1 + 2x_2 \geq 16$$
   $$x_1, x_2 \geq 0$$

Solution

First notice that the problem is a minimization problem with two $\geq$ constraints. For each $\geq$ constraint, a surplus variable must be subtracted to make the constraint an equality, and an artificial variable must be added to create a starting basis. The objective function coefficients of the surplus variables are 0 and of the artificials are M. The problem, ready for simplex, is:

   minimize $Z = 2x_1 + 3x_2 + 0s_1 + 0s_2 + MA_1 + MA_2$
   subject to
   $$x_1 + x_2 - s_1 + A_1 = 6$$
   $$4x_1 + 2x_2 - s_2 + A_2 = 16$$
   $$x_1, x_2, s_1, s_2, A_1, A_2 \geq 0$$

The initial simplex tableau is shown in table 5.1.

Table 5.1 Initial Simplex Tableau

c_j			2	3	0	0	M	M
	basic variables	quantity	x_1	x_2	s_1	s_2	A_1	A_2
M	A_1	6	1	1	−1	0	1	0
M	A_2	16	4	2	0	−1	0	1
	z_j	22M	5M	3M	−M	−M	M	M
	$z_j - c_j$		5M−2	3M−3	−M	−M	0	0

The Minimization Problem and Irregular Types of
Linear Programming Problems

Since M is a very large positive number, $5M-2$ is larger than $3M-3$, and x_1 will enter the basis. Since $16/4$ is smaller than $6/1$, x_1 will replace A_2. The next tableau is shown in table 5.2 after the row operations have been completed. Notice the column for A_2 has been dropped.

Table 5.2 Second Simplex Tableau

c_j			2	3	0	0	M
	basic variables	quantity	x_1	x_2	s_1	s_2	A_1
M	A_1	2	0	1/2	-1	1/4	1
2	x_1	4	1	1/2	0	$-1/4$	0
	z_j	2M+8	2	M/2+1	$-M$	M/4$-$1/2	M
	z_j-c_j		0	M/2$-$2	$-M$	M/4$-$1/2	0

The solution is not yet optimal since there are positive entries in the bottom (z_j-c_j) row. For the next tableau, x_2 will enter the basis and A_1 will leave. The third tableau is shown in table 5.3.

Table 5.3 Third Simplex Tableau

c_j			2	3	0	0
	basic variables	quantity	x_1	x_2	s_1	s_2
3	x_2	4	0	1	-2	1/2
2	x_1	2	1	0	$+1$	$-1/2$
	z_j	16	2	3	-4	1/2
	z_j-c_j		0	0	-4	1/2

Another iteration is necessary since the s_2 column has a positive entry in the z_j-c_j row. This time, s_2 will enter the basis and x_1 will leave. The fourth tableau is in table 5.4.

Table 5.4 Optimal Simplex Tableau

c_j			2	3	0	0
	basic variables	quantity	x_1	x_2	s_1	s_2
0	s_2	8	0	2	-4	1
2	x_1	6	1	1	-1	0
	z_j	12	2	2	-2	0
	z_j-c_j		0	-6	-2	0

The optimal solution $x_1=6$, $x_2=0, s_1=0, s_2=8, A_1=0, A_2=0$ has been found. The value of the objective function is 12.

2. Solve the following problem by using the simplex algorithm:

maximize $Z = x_1 + x_2$
subject to
$$5x_1 + 3x_2 \leq 30$$
$$x_1 + x_2 \leq 8$$
$$10x_1 - 3x_2 \geq 15$$
$$x_1, x_2 \geq 0$$

Solution

After converting the three inequalities to equalities, we see that it is necessary to add an artificial variable to the third constraint to create an initial basis. The first simplex tableau is shown in table 5.5.

Table 5.5 The Initial Simplex Tableau

c_j	basic variables	quantity	1 x_1	1 x_2	0 s_1	0 s_2	0 s_3	$-M$ A_1
0	s_1	30	5	3	1	0	0	0
0	s_2	8	1	1	0	1	0	0
$-M$	A_1	15	10	-3	0	0	-1	1
	z_j	$-15M$	$-10M$	$3M$	0	0	M	$-M$
	c_j-z_j		$10M+1$	$-3M+1$	0	0	$-M$	0

The remaining simplex tableaus are shown in tables 5.6 and 5.7.

Table 5.6 The Second Simplex Tableau

c_j	basic variables	quantity	1 x_1	1 x_2	0 s_1	0 s_2	0 s_3
0	s_1	45/2	0	9/2	1	0	1/2
0	s_2	13/2	0	13/10	0	1	1/10
1	x_1	3/2	1	$-3/10$	0	0	$-1/10$
	z_j	3/2	1	$-3/10$	0	0	$-1/10$
	c_j-z_j		0	13/10	0	0	1/10

Table 5.7 The Third Simplex Tableau

c_j	basic variables	quantity	1 x_1	1 x_2	0 s_1	0 s_2	0 s_3
0	s_1	0	0	0	1	$-45/13$	2/13
1	x_2	5	0	1	0	10/13	1/13
1	x_1	3	1	0	0	3/13	$-1/13$
	z_j	8	1	1	0	1	0
	c_j-z_j		0	0	0	-1	0

Because we no longer have any positive entries in the c_j-z_j row, we know that the optimal solution has been reached. The value of Z is 8. However, there is a zero in the c_j-z_j row in the s_3 column, which means that a new solution, with s_3 in the basis and the same value of Z, does exist. Hence, this problem has alternative optimal solutions. To find the other "corner point" of the set of optimal solutions, let s_3 enter the basis. See table 5.8.

Table 5.8 The Fourth Simplex Tableau

c_j			1	1	0	0	0
	basic variables	quantity	x_1	x_2	s_1	s_2	s_3
0	s_3	0	0	0	13/2	−45/2	1
1	x_2	5	0	1	−1/2	5/2	0
1	x_1	3	1	0	1/2	−3/2	0
	z_j	8	1	1	0	1	0
	$c_j - z_j$		0	0	0	−1	0

Case *JB Cartage Company*

The JB Cartage Company had expanded its fleet of large dump trucks and, in the spring of 1981, was aggressively seeking new contracts. The new trucks were specifically designed to haul coal, but could be used for other material. A contract that JB was particularly interested in obtaining was that with the state university. Bids were currently being taken for the transfer of the winter's coal supply from two mines to the university's main and regional campuses.

John Blackburn, president and founder of JB, had always determined bids on a cost-plus basis. The bid for the university would not be any different, except that the amount added would be somewhat smaller, in hopes of increasing the likelihood of having the bid accepted. While John was not willing to take a loss on the venture, he also was anxious to establish himself with the university and utilize his fleet.

As a first step in developing his price, John decided to find the most efficient way that the coal could be transferred from the two mines to the two campuses. If these shipping routes could be determined in such a way as to minimize total mileage, John knew he could develop a low bid. The information he had to work with is shown in exhibits 5.1 and 5.2.

Exhibit 5.1 Distances from Mines to Campuses (in Miles)

Mine	Main Campus	Regional Campus
Big Vein	150	100
Andrews Creek	70	120

Exhibit 5.2 Coal Availability and Demand (in Truckloads)

Mine	Coal Available	Campus	Coal Needed
Big Vein	120	Main	150
Andrews Creek	180	Regional	100

The Minimization Problem and Irregular Types of Linear Programming Problems

6 Postoptimality Analysis

Key Concepts

I. The analysis of the optimal simplex solution, to gather additional information of use to the decision maker, is called *postoptimality analysis*.

   A. Every linear programming problem called the *primal problem* is associated with another linear programming problem called the *dual problem*.

      1. The dual problem is constructed from the primal according to specific rules, but, in general, the sense of the optimization switches, right-hand side values switch with constraint coefficients, the rows of constraints become columns, and the columns become rows.

      2. The variables of the dual problem represent the *marginal value* of another unit of resource and, as a result, can help the decision maker evaluate and control the use of resources.

   B. *Sensitivity analysis* allows a decision maker to see what effect a change in a parameter, such as an objective function or constraint quantity, would have on the solution of the problem.

      1. In order to see how much an objective function coefficient can change before the currently optimal basis would no longer be optimal, it is necessary to add a variable amount, Δ, to the objective function coefficient and all that it influences in the final tableau.

      2. The range of permissible values for Δ, and hence for the coefficient, are determined by choosing Δ so that all entries in the $c_j - z_j$ row remain negative or zero.

      3. In order to see how much a constraint quantity can change before the currently optimal basis would no longer be optimal, add the final tableau values (including signs) in the column of the slack variable associated with the constraint whose quantity is being evaluated, multiplied by Δ, to the final tableau quantity values.

      4. The resulting quantities must remain nonnegative, so the range on Δ, and hence on the original quantity, may be determined by choosing Δ so that all entries in the quantity column remain nonnegative.

II. Sensitivity analysis and duality can be utilized together to tell over what range the shadow prices are valid and therefore help managers evaluate alternatives.

Quiz

True-False

T F   1. When a primal problem has three decision variables and two constraints, the dual problem will have two decision variables and three constraints.

T **F**   2. When the primal problem is a maximization problem and the dual problem is a minimization problem, the optimal objective function value of the primal will be higher than the optimal objective function value of the dual.

T F   3. Each dual variable is associated with a specific primal constraint.

T F   4. Sensitivity analysis allows decision makers to see how sensitive their problem solutions are to changes in the environment.

T **F**   5. It is necessary to start over and redo the simplex operations from the beginning to see what effect would be had by a change in a quantity value.

T F   6. As long as Δ for an objective function coefficient is within the boundaries so that all entries in the $c_j - z_j$ row remain negative or zero, the values of the decision variables will remain constant, but the total profit might change.

T (F)   7. As long as Δ for a right-hand side is within the boundaries so that all entries in the quantity column remain nonnegative, the values of the decision variables will remain constant, but the total profit might change.

Exercises

8. Write the dual to the following primal problem.

maximize $Z = x_1 + 6x_2 + 4x_3$
subject to
1) $2x_1 - 3x_2 + x_3 \leq 26$
2) $x_1 + x_2 + x_3 \leq 18$
3) $x_1, x_2, x_3 \geq 0$

[handwritten:]
MIN $Z = 26y_1 + 18y_2$
$2y_1 + y_2 \geq 1$
$-3y_1 + y_2 \geq 6$
$x_1 + y_2 \geq 4$

9. Write the dual to the following primal problem.

minimize $Z = 14x_1 + 12x_2$
subject to
1) $x_1 + x_2 \geq 100$
2) $2x_1 - x_2 \geq 0$
3) $4x_1 + 6x_2 \geq 500$
4) $x_1, x_2 \geq 0$

[handwritten:]
MAX $Z = 100y_1 + 0y_2 + 500y_3$
$y_1 + 2y_2 + 4y_3 \leq 14$
$y_1 - y_2 + 6y_3 \leq 12$

10. After doing sensitivity in a problem on the c_1 coefficient, you find the following entries in the $c_j - z_j$ row.

$-12 + 2\Delta$ *[handwritten:]* $2\Delta = 12$ $\Delta = 6$
$-5 - 5\Delta$ *[handwritten:]* $-5\Delta = 5$ $\Delta = -1$
$-2 + 2\Delta/3$ *[handwritten:]* $2/3\Delta = 2$ $\Delta = 3$
$-1 - \Delta/2$ *[handwritten:]* $-1/2\Delta = 1$ $\Delta = -2$

[handwritten:] $-1 \leq \Delta \leq 3$

Over what range can Δ vary and still have the current basis remain optimal?   *[handwritten:]* $15 \leq C_1 \leq 19$

11. If the original value of c_1 from question 10 had been 16, what range of values are permissible for c_1?

12. After doing sensitivity in a problem on the b_1 coefficient, you find the following entries in the quantity column.

Basic Variables	Quantity		
x_1	$10 + \Delta/2$	*[hw]* $1/2\Delta = -10$	$\Delta = -20$
x_2	$6 - \Delta/2$	*[hw]* $1/2\Delta = 6$	$\Delta = 12$
x_3	$15 + 2\Delta$	*[hw]* $2\Delta = -15$	$\Delta = -15/2 = -7.5$

Over what range can Δ vary and still have the current basis remain optimal?   *[handwritten:]* $-15/2 \leq \Delta \leq 12$

13. If the original value of b_1 in question 12 had been 20, what range of values are permissible for b_1? *[handwritten:]* $25/2 \leq b_1 \leq 32$

14. If b_1 in question 12 changes from its original 20 to 16, what are the new optimal values of the decision variables?

[handwritten:]
$x_1 = 8$
$x_2 = 8$
$x_3 = 7$

Problems

1. The following situation exists:

Resource	Resource Requirements		Total Available
	Product 1	Product 2	
1	10	12	200
2	5	3	90
3	2	6	100
Profit	$50	$100	

a. Write the primal linear programming model.
b. Write the dual model.
c. Explain the units of the dual model.

(handwritten, top right)
$MAX\ Z = 50X_1 + 100X_2$
$10X_1 + 12X_2 \le 200$
$5X_1 + 3X_2 \le 90$
$2X_1 + 6X_2 \le 100$

Solution

a. The primal model is:

maximize $Z = \$50x_1 + \$100x_2$
subject to
$$10x_1 + 12x_2 \le 200$$
$$5x_1 + 3x_2 \le 90$$
$$2x_1 + 6x_2 \le 100$$
$$x_1, x_2 \ge 0$$

(handwritten, right)
$MIN\ Z = 200Y_1 + 90Y_2 + 100Y_3$
$10X_1 + 5Y_2 + 2Y_3 \ge 50$
$12Y_1 + 3Y_2 + 6Y_3 \ge 100$

b. To form the dual model, first realize that the primal problem is a maximization with all less-than-or-equal-to constraints, so the dual model will be a minimization with all greater-than-or-equal-to constraints. Since there are two primal variables and three constraints, the dual will have three variables and two constraints. After placing the coefficients in the proper place, we have as the dual model:

minimize $Z = 200y_1 + 90y_2 + 100y_3$
subject to
$$10y_1 + 5y_2 + 2y_3 \ge 50$$
$$12y_1 + 3y_2 + 6y_3 \ge 100$$
$$y_1, y_2, y_3 \ge 0$$

c. The units of the dual model are:

y_1 = the dollar value of a unit of resource #1
y_2 = the dollar value of a unit of resource #2
y_3 = the dollar value of a unit of resource #3

2. In chapter 4, the following problem was solved by the simplex procedure.

maximize $Z = x_1 + 2x_2 + 4x_3$
subject to
$$2x_1 + x_2 + 3x_3 \le 12$$
$$4x_1 + x_2 + x_3 \le 6$$
$$x_1, x_2, x_3 \ge 0$$

(handwritten, right)
$-5 - 5\Delta \to$ $-5\Delta = 5$ $\Delta = -1$
$\Delta/2 = 1$ $\Delta = 2$
$-3/2\ \Delta = 1$ $\Delta = -2/3$

$\Delta = -6$

The final tableau was:

(handwritten, right)
$3 + 1/2\ \Delta \ge 0$ $1/2\Delta \ge -3$
$3 - 1/2\ \Delta \ge 0$ $-1/2\Delta \ge -3$
$\Delta \le 6$

c_j			1	2 + Δ	4	0	0
	basic variables	quantity	x_1	x_2	x_3	s_1	s_2
4	x_3	3	−1	0	1	1/2	−1/2
2 + Δ	x_2	3	5	1	0	−1/2	3/2
	z_j	18 + 3Δ	6 + 5Δ	2 + Δ	4	1 − Δ/2	1 + 3/2 Δ
	$c_j - z_j$	21	−5 − 5Δ	0	0	−1 + Δ/2	−1 − 3/2 Δ

(handwritten, right)
$2 - 1 - \frac{\Delta}{2} = 1 - \Delta/2$
$-2 + 3 + 3/2\ \Delta = 1 + 3/2\Delta$

$4/3 \le c_2 \le 4$
$-2/3 \le \Delta \le 2$

a. By how much can the coefficient of x_2, c_2, change without causing a change in the solution?
b. What will the solution to this problem be if c_2 changes from 2 to 3?   *(handwritten)* $Z = 21$
c. By how much can the first constraint's quantity value, q_1, change without causing a change in the optimal basis?
   (handwritten) $b \le q_1 \le 18$
d. What will the optimal solution be if q_1 changes from 12 to 8?

(handwritten, bottom)
$3 + \left(-4/2\right) = 1$
$3 - -4/2 = 5$
$Z = 14$

Solution

a. To see what happens if c_2 changes from 2 to $2 + \Delta$, replace the 2 in the c_j column and row by $2 + \Delta$ and refigure the z_j and $c_j - z_j$ rows.

z_j	$18 + 3\Delta$	$6 + 5\Delta$	$2 + \Delta$	4	$1 - 1/2\Delta$	$1 + 3/2\Delta$
$c_j - z_j$		$-5 - 5\Delta$	0	0	$-1 + 1/2\Delta$	$-1 - 3/2\Delta$

In order for the current basis to remain optimal, the entries in the $c_j - z_j$ row must remain nonpositive, so Δ will be determined so that:

$$-5 - 5\Delta \le 0$$
$$-1 + 1/2\Delta \le 0$$
$$-1 - 3/2\Delta \le 0$$

Solving these three inequalities for Δ, we see that:

$$\Delta \ge -1$$
$$\Delta \le 2$$
$$\Delta \ge -2/3$$

Therefore, in order for none of the inequalities to be violated, we must have $-2/3 \le \Delta \le 2$, and then $4/3 \le c_2 \le 4$.

b. The value of 3 for c_2 is within the range found in part a. The only change will be that the revised value of Z will be $18 + 3\Delta = 18 + 3(1) = 21$.

c. To see how much the value of q_1 can change, first realize that s_1 is the slack variable associated with constraint 1 and so it is the s_1 column in the final tableau (times Δ) that will be appended to the quantity column. Since the quantity values can never be negative, the restrictions for Δ are found from:

$$x_3 = 3 + 1/2\Delta \ge 0$$
$$x_2 = 3 - 1/2\Delta \ge 0$$

Solving for Δ, we see that:

$$\Delta \ge -6$$
$$\Delta \le 6$$

Therefore $-6 \le \Delta \le 6$, and $6 \le q_1 \le 18$.

d. If q_1 changes from 12 to 8, Δ will be -4. That value is within the permissible range for Δ. The new solution, which maintains the optimal basis variables, will be:

$$x_3 = 3 + 1/2\,(-4) = 1$$
$$x_2 = 3 - 1/2\,(-4) = 5$$
$$Z = 18 + 1\,(-4) = 14$$

Notice that the shadow price for the first constraint, or the value of y, if we were to write the dual problem, is 1. This means that the value of a unit of constraint #1 material is worth 1, and if we reduce our supply by four units, from 12 to 8, the profit will decrease by $4 = 4$ units ($1/unit). *Note:* The values of the shadow prices are accurate only as long as the number of units evaluated remains within the range found for Δ.

Appendix B illustrates sensitivity analysis for this problem as it is done by the MPOS computer package. The tables give the ranges and corresponding changes in the objective function.

It was shortly before noon when David Walters returned Jane Kendrick's phone call. Walters had solved the linear programming problem and was ready to tell Kendrick that the best he could do would be supply 10 large trashcans and 50 dustpans.

"Ms. Kendrick's office. This is Mrs. Richards speaking."

"This is David Walters calling, Mrs. Richards. Is Ms. Kendrick in?"

"I'm sorry, Mr. Walters. Ms. Kendrick had to go to lunch with the president, but she did leave a message for you. She talked to Jones in Chicago, and while they can take care of supplying us, they're going to tack on an extremely large expediting and delivery charge. Ms. Kendrick asked that you use this information to see if it changes the outlook any on your end."

"All right, Mrs. Richards, I'll see what I can come up with," Walters said. "Will you have her call me when she gets back to the office?"

"Certainly, Mr. Walters."

Walters mumbled grumpily to himself as he pulled out his notes. "See what we can do. Ha! There are alot of ways to go on this. We could raise the price, but she needs to get something for it. What we really need is more time in cutting and finishing, but how much, and how much is it worth to us? I'd better get busy on this one. Glad I saved the final tableau from the original problem."

7 Transportation and Assignment Problems

Key Concepts

I. The transportation problem is a special type of linear programming problem whose structure allows it to be solved by a technique that is much simpler than the simplex algorithm.

  A. The structure of the transportation problem involves a product to be transported from a number of sources to a number of destinations, each of which has a fixed amount of supply and demand, at the minimum possible cost.

  B. To solve the problem, a table is constructed with supply sources in the rows, demand destinations in the columns, the cells representing the amount shipped from the corresponding source to the corresponding destination, and the cost of each route noted in the upper corner of the corresponding cell.

  C. One of three methods may be followed to find an initial solution.

   1. The northwest corner method finds an initial feasible solution by shipping as much as possible in the upper left (northwest) cell of the table, then moving down or to the right to fill supply or demand until all rim requirements have been met.

   2. The minimum cell cost method first allocates as much as possible to the cell with the lowest cost, then to the feasible cell with the next lowest cost, and so forth until all rim requirements have been met.

   3. To use Vogel's Approximation Method, first compute the penalty cost for each row and column, select the row or column with the highest penalty cost, allocate as much as possible to the feasible cell with the lowest transportation cost in that row or column, and repeat until all rim requirements have been met.

  D. One of two methods may be used to improve the initial feasible solution to find the optimal solution.

   1. The stepping stone method evaluates all empty cells.

     a. The stepping stone method evaluates the net change in unit cost from having allocated a unit to an empty cell, and then adjusting other allocations through a stepping stone pattern to maintain the rim requirements.

     b. The cell with the most cost reduction will be chosen to be the entering variable.

     c. The cell in the path that most limits the amount we could allocate to the entering cell will leave, or no longer be an active route.

     d. These steps repeat until no path is left that shows any improvement.

   2. The Modified Distribution Method (MODI) mathematically determines cell cost changes without identifying all stepping stone paths.

     a. Values of u_i (for supply) and v_j (for demand) are determined so that $u_i + v_j = c_{ij}$ in every cell in which there is a shipment, letting $u_1 = 0$.

     b. For empty cells calculate $k = c_{ij} - u_i - v_j$ and let the cell with the largest negative k be the entering variable.

     c. Determine the closed loop path that will result and make the necessary allocation to ship as much as possible in the entering cell.

     d. Repeat until no cell has a negative value of k.

  E. Some transportation problems require special treatment.

   1. Unbalanced transportation problems need to have a dummy supply row or demand column (with cell costs of 0) added to make total supply equal total demand.

   2. When fewer than $m + n - 1$ cells are filled, a degenerate solution exists. To compensate for this, a cell (which will allow us to complete the assigning of the u's and v's and find stepping stone paths) must be artificially designated as having an allocation.

   3. If any route is prohibited, it should be assigned a large positive cost of m to prevent its being selected as an entering variable.

   4. Alternate optimal solutions exist if, in the final solution, a value of k is zero. Find the other solution by letting that cell enter the basis.

II. The assignment problem is similar to the transportation problem except that each supply and demand are limited to only one unit.
  A. To solve the problem several steps must be followed.
    1. Perform row reductions by subtracting the smallest cost in each row from all others in that row, then column reductions by subtracting the smallest (reduced) cost in each column from all others in that column.
    2. Draw the minimum number of horizontal and/or vertical lines to cover all the zeros. If there are as many lines as assignments, report the optimal assignment by locating the zeros.
    3. If there are fewer lines than assignments, find the minimum unlined cost, subtract it from all other unlined costs, add it to all double-lined costs, and recopy all the single-lined costs, then go to step 2.
  B. Some assignment problems require special treatment.
    1. If the problem is unbalanced, dummy rows or columns should be added, at zero cost, to make the problem square.
    2. Prohibited assignments are given a cost of m.

Quiz

True-False

T F   1. A transportation problem must have the same number of sources as destinations.

T F   2. A transportation problem must have total supply equal to total demand.

T F   3. There is no guarantee that one of the three methods for finding an initial solution to a transportation problem will be more efficient than any other method.

T F   4. In the MODI method, the optimal solution has been reached when $u_i + v_j \leq c_{ij}$, for all values of i and j.

T F   5. Assignment problems can be solved by the same methods used to solve transportation problems.

T F   6. An assignment problem must have the same number of sources as destinations.

Short Answer

7. How are unacceptable routes handled in a transportation problem?

8. How are unacceptable routes handled in an assignment problem?

9. What should be done if fewer than the number of rows plus the number of columns minus 1 cells are being used in a transportation problem?

10. Is a transportation problem ever infeasible?

Table 7.1 Information for Questions 11–15

u_i	v_i / From	$v_A=$ / A	$v_B=$ / B	$v_C=$ / C	Supply
$u_1=$	1	5 / 20	8 / 20	3 /	40
$u_2=$	2	6 /	7 / 10	5 / 50	60
	Demand	20	30	50	

11. What is the cost of the current shipping pattern?

12. Determine u_1, u_2, v_A, v_B, and v_C.

13. Is this shipping pattern optimal?

14. What cell should be used in order to improve the solution?

15. (Advanced) Write the general linear programming formulation of a transportation problem using the problem in table 7.1. Write the dual to this problem. Do you see how the MODI method was invented?

Problems

1. Solve the following transportation problem. Drums of solvent are produced in factories in Indianapolis, Gary, and Cincinnati and need to be shipped to assembly plants in Fort Wayne, Lafayette, and Evansville. Supply and demand are defined in each location, and they and the intercity costs are shown below.

From	To Fort Wayne	Lafayette	Evansville	Supply
Indianapolis	100	50	90	200
Gary	100	80	200	500
Cincinnati	140	120	80	300
Demand	350	150	400	

Solution

Any of the three initial solution methods and two solution procedures could be used. For illustration purposes, we will show the northwest corner method and the MODI method. The initial solution is shown in table 7.2. A dummy demand location is necessary since total supply equals 1,000 and total demand equals 900.

Table 7.2 Northwest Corner Solution

To From	Fort Wayne	Lafayette	Evansville	Dummy	Supply
Indianapolis	100 / 200	50	90	0	200
Gary	100 / 150	80 / 150	200 / 200	0	500
Cincinnati	140	120	80 / 200	0 / 100	300
Demand	350	150	400	100	1000

To see if the current solution is optimal, we must assign the u_i and v_j values, starting with $u_i = 0$, so that $u_i + v_j = c_{ij}$ wherever there is a shipment. This is shown in table 7.3.

Table 7.3 The u_i and v_j Values

u_i	v_j To From	$v_F = 100$ Fort Wayne	$v_L = 80$ Lafayette	$v_E = 200$ Evansville	$v_D = 120$ Dummy	Supply
$u_i = 0$	Indianapolis	100 / 200	50	90	0	200
$u_G = 0$	Gary	100 / 150	80 / 150	− 200 / 200 +	0	500
$u_C = -120$	Cincinnati	140	120	+ 80 / 200 −	0 / 100	300
	Demand	350	150	400	100	1000

The cost changes for the unoccupied cells are:

x_{IL}: $50-0-80 = -30$ x_{GD}: $0-0-120 = -120$
x_{IE}: $90-0-200 = -110$ x_{CF}: $140-(-120)-100 = +160$
x_{ID}: $0-0-120 = -120$ x_{CL}: $120-(-120)-80 = +160$

There is a tie between x_{ID} and x_{GD} as the entering variables. Although the solution of a tie is arbitrary, we will choose x_{GD} to enter because the resulting stepping stone path is simpler. The path is shown in table 7.3. Since each unit we ship from Gary to dummy will save \$120, we want to ship as many as possible, or 100 units. The resulting solution, along with its u_i and v_j values, is shown in table 7.4.

Table 7.4   Second Iteration

u_i	v_j / To From	$v_F = 100$ Fort Wayne	$v_L = 80$ Lafayette	$v_E = 200$ Evansville	$v_D = 0$ Dummy	Supply
$u_I = 0$	Indianapolis	− 100 200	50	+ 90	0	200
$u_G = 0$	Gary	+ 100 150	80 150	− 200 100	0 100	500
$u_C = -120$	Cincinnati	140	120	80 300	0	300
	Demand	350	150	400	100	1000

The cost changes for the unoccupied cells are:

x_{IL}: $50-0-80 = -30$ x_{CF}: $140-(-120)-100 = +160$
x_{IE}: $90-0-200 = -110$ x_{CL}: $120-(-120)-80 = +160$
x_{ID}: $0-0-0 = 0$ x_{CD}: $0-(-120)-0 = +120$

The new shipment will be from Indianapolis to Evansville, and the stepping stone path tells us that the amount shipped will be 100 units. The new solution is shown in table 7.5.

Table 7.5   Third Iteration

u_i	v_j / To From	$v_F = 100$ Fort Wayne	$v_L = 80$ Lafayette	$v_E = 90$ Evansville	$v_D = 0$ Dummy	Supply
$u_I = 0$	Indianapolis	− 100 100	+ 50	90 100	0	200
$u_G = 0$	Gary	+ 100 250	− 80 150	200	0 100	500
$u_C = -10$	Cincinnati	140	120	80 300	0	300
	Demand	350	150	400	100	1000

The cost changes for the unoccupied cells are:

x_{IL}: $50-0-80 = -30$ x_{CF}: $140-(-10)-100 = +50$
x_{ID}: $0-0-0 = 0$ x_{CL}: $120-(-10)-80 = +50$
x_{GE}: $200-0-90 = +110$ x_{CD}: $0-(-10)-0 = +10$

The new shipment will be from Indianapolis to Lafayette, and the stepping stone path tells us that the amount shipped will be 100 units. The new solution is shown in table 7.6.

Table 7.6 Fourth Iteration

u_i / v_j	To / From	$v_F=70$ Fort Wayne	$v_L=50$ Lafayette	$v_E=90$ Evansville	$v_D=-30$ Dummy	Supply
$u_I=0$	Indianapolis	100	50 / 100	90 / 100	0	200
$u_G=30$	Gary	100 / 350	80 / 50	200	0 / 100	500
$u_C=-10$	Cincinnati	140	120	80 / 300	0	300
	Demand	350	150	400	100	1000

The cost changes for the unoccupied cells are:

x_{IF}: $100-0-70 = +30$ $\qquad$ x_{CF}: $140-(-10)-70 = +80$

x_{ID}: $0-0-(-30) = +30$ $\qquad$ x_{CL}: $120-(-10)-50 = +80$

x_{GE}: $200-30-90 = +80$ $\qquad$ x_{CD}: $0-(-10)-(-30) = +40$

Since none of the $c_{ij}-u_i-v_j$ values is negative, we have found the optimal solution to the problem. The cost is:

$$100(50) + 100(90) + 350(100) + 50(80) + 300(8) = \$77,000$$

2. Solve the following assignment problem to allocate workers to jobs in such a way as to minimize completion time.

Workers	Jobs 1	Jobs 2	Jobs 3
Anderson	6	3	10
Beasley	3	2	8
Craddock	8	2	5
Davidson	7	6	9

Solution

You first should notice that, since there are four workers and only three jobs, a dummy job must be created, with costs (times) of zero, as shown in table 7.7.

Table 7.7. Problem with Dummy Job Added

Workers	Jobs 1	Jobs 2	Jobs 3	Dummy
Anderson	6	3	10	0
Beasley	3	2	8	0
Craddock	8	2	5	0
Davidson	7	6	9	0

Table 7.8 Problem after Column Reduction

Workers	Jobs 1	Jobs 2	Jobs 3	Dummy
Anderson	3	1	5	0
Beasley	0	0	3	0
Craddock	5	0	0	0
Davidson	4	4	4	0

Transportation and Assignment Problems

Since the minimum cost in each row is zero, row reductions would not change the problem. The minimum cost in each of the columns (3, 2, 5, and 0) would then be subtracted. The resulting cost table is shown in table 7.8. To cover all of the zeros in table 7.8 requires only three lines. The smallest cost that is not covered by a line is 1. Adding and subtracting that 1 where indicated results in table 7.9.

Table 7.9 Problem after Iteration

	Jobs			
Workers	1	2	3	Dummy
Anderson	2	0	4	0
Beasley	0	0	3	1
Craddock	5	0	0	1
Davidson	3	3	3	0

At this stage, four lines are required to cover the zeros, so we are done. To find the optimal assignment, start with those workers who are limited to only one job.

Davidson must be idle (dummy).
Therefore, Anderson must do job 2.
Therefore, Beasley can only do job 1.
Therefore, Craddock must do job 3.
The total time is $3 + 3 + 5 + 0 = 11$.

Case *Post County Public Library*

The Post County Public Library consisted of a main library, four branches, and a media mobile and provided services for several adjoining counties.

The main branch of the library had moved into a new building in March 1979, allowing space for a large increase in collections, staff, and patron usage. As director of circulation for the main library, Jane Holder was responsible for overseeing much of the library's interaction with the public. The circulation department processed applications for library cards, checked out the books, kept track of reserve and overdue books, checked in the books, and maintained the general collections.

The library was located in a college town, so many of Holder's employees were students who were glad to get part-time jobs. While the library was willing to hire part-time employees, the fact that many of the students were from out of town and would not be working over the Christmas holidays caused problems in staffing the circulation department. The holiday period also saw a large increase in library usage, with local school children on vacation.

The Monday morning between Christmas and New Year's Day presented a typical holiday headache for Holder. She knew that each of the six employees working that day would have to spend time shelving the books that had been returned over the weekend. However, before that task was begun, five other jobs had to be finished. Holder wanted to assign each of the five jobs to a different person, leaving the sixth person free to check out books to patrons.

The jobs that needed to be done were:

1. Separating and filing library card applications by name and number.
2. Typing letters for overdue material.
3. Carding returned books.
4. "Running the well" for reserves (searching for the status of requested books).
5. Alphabetizing book cards.

Because the six available employees were not necessarily the ones who usually performed these tasks, Holder knew she would have to estimate how long it would take for each employee to complete each job before she could assign the jobs. As she prepared the times shown in exhibit 1, she also remembered that John was not really an accurate enough typist to be able to type the overdue notices and that Mary had done so much alphabetizing the previous week that she really should not be asked to do any more.

Exhibit 1 Times to Complete Jobs (in minutes)

Person	Job 1	2	3	4	5
Jane	25	45	60	90	40
Randy	30	50	65	85	40
Wilma	25	55	80	80	45
Mary	35	50	60	95	—
John	20	—	50	90	50
Lisa	30	50	65	80	45

Transportation and Assignment Problems

8 Integer Programming

Key Concepts

I. *Integer programming* is a type of linear programming used in problems for which fractional values for the decision variables do not make sense.

   A. *Total integer models* are those in which all decision variables must have integer values as their optimal solutions.

   B. *Mixed integer models* require only some of their decision variables to have integer values.

   C. For *0 − 1 integer models,* the variable values are restricted to either 0 or 1, a technique useful in designating "go-no go" decisions.

II. Since the simplex solution of an integer programming problem rarely automatically yields an integer solution, and the rounding of noninteger solutions is not guaranteed to give the optimal integer solution, the *branch and bound method* has been developed as a solution procedure for integer programming problems.

   A. In total integer problems, follow the steps below for the branch and bound method.

      1. Find the optimal simplex solution to the linear programming model with the integer restrictions *relaxed.*

      2. At node 1 let the relaxed simplex solution be the upper bound and the "rounded down" integer solution be the lower bound.

      3. Select the variable with the greatest fractional part for branching. Create two new constraints for this variable reflecting the partitioned integer values for this variable. This will result in a new "≤" constraint and a new "≥" constraint.

      4. Create two new nodes—one for the "≥" constraint and one for the "≤" constraint.

      5. Solve the "relaxed" linear programming model with the new constraint added to each of these nodes.

      6. The relaxed simplex solution is the upper bound at each node and the *existing* maximum integer solution (at any node) is the lower bound.

      7. If a feasible integer solution exists with the greatest upper bound value of any ending node, the optimal integer solution has been reached. If a feasible integer solution does not exist, branch from the node with the greatest upper bound.

      8. Return to step 3.

   B. To solve the mixed integer problem by branch and bound, only round or compare fractional parts of those variables required to be integer.

   C. To solve the 0−1 integer problem by branch and bound, add the constraint $x_j \leq 1$ for each 0−1 decision variable to the original problem. Branching constraints will be $x_j = 0$ and $x_j = 1$.

Quiz

Short Answer

1. Explain the difference between total integer, mixed integer, and 0−1 integer programming models.

2. Is rounding the solutions found by the simplex procedure a good method for finding the integer solution to a problem?

3. Explain how complete enumeration is used to solve some integer programming problems.

4. What is implicit enumeration?

5. What happens if, during the branch and bound procedure, a problem has no feasible solution?

6. How do you know which variable to use for the branching procedure?

7. How do you know when you have reached the optimal solution using branch and bound?

8. The optimal solution to a total integer programming problem with relaxed constraints is $x_1 = 2.33, x_2 = 8.25$. What two constraints should be written to do the branching?

9. If only x_2 had been required to be integer in question 8, what would the two constraints be?

10. When the solution is found at any node of a branch and bound problem, how do you determine whether the solution will be an upper bound or a lower bound?

Problems

1. The Knox Company is doing capital budgeting to decide which of five investments should be made during the coming year to maximize return. The investments, their costs, and estimated net returns are summarized below. The company has $100,000 available. Formulate the integer programming problem.

Investment	Unit Cost	Unit Return
Remodel plant	$50,000	$10,000
Buy machine A	5,000	2,500
Buy machine B	15,000	10,000
Invest in bonds	1,000	150
Acquire company C	75,000	20,000

Note: Machine B can be used only if the plant is remodelled.

Solution

Let x_1 = 1 if the plant is remodelled
    = 0 if not
 x_2 = 1 if machine A is purchased
    = 0 if not
 x_3 = 1 if machine B is purchased
    = 0 if not
 x_4 = the number of $1,000 bonds purchased
 x_5 = 1 if company C is acquired
    = 0 if not

Our objective is to maximize return, so the objective function would be:

maximize $Z = 10,000x_1 + 2,500x_2 + 10,000x_3 + 150x_4 + 20,000x_5$

Since there is $100,000 available for investment, one constraint would be:

$50,000x_1 + 5,000x_2 + 15,000x_3 + 1,000x_4 + 75,000x_5 \leq 100,000$

To write the constraint that deals with machine B and the remodelling, we realize that if x_3 = 1, then x_1 must equal 1, but we can have x_3 = 0 and x_1 = 1, or both x_3 = 0 and x_1 = 0. This means $x_3 \leq x_1$ or $-x_1 + x_3 \leq 0$.
The integer programming model is:

maximize $Z = 10,000x_1 + 2,500x_2 + 10,000x_3 + 150x_4 + 20,000x_5$
subject to
$50,000x_1 + 5,000x_2 + 150,000x_3 + 1,000x_4 + 75,000x_5 \leq 1,000,000$
$$-x_1 + x_3 \leq 0$$

where x_1, x_2, x_3, x_5 are 0 or 1 and $x_4 \geq 0$ and integer.

2. Solve the following integer programming problem by the branch and bound method.

maximize $Z = 5x_1 + 6x_2$
subject to
$2x_1 + 3x_2 \leq 12$
$5x_1 + 4x_2 \leq 25$
$x_1, x_2 \geq 0$

Solution

First solve the problem as a linear programming problem. The final tableau is shown in table 8.1.

Table 8.1 The Optimal "Relaxed" Simplex Solution

c_j			5	6	0	0
	basic variable	quantity	x_1	x_2	s_1	s_2
6	x_2	10/7	0	1	5/7	−2/7
5	x_1	27/7	1	0	−4/7	3/7
	z_j	249/7	5	6	10/7	3/7
	$c_j − z_j$		0	0	−10/7	−3/7

The upper bound for the problem is $249/7 = 35.57$, and the lower bound, by rounding down x_1 to 3 and x_2 to 1, is 21. Node 1 is shown in figure 8.1.

Figure 8.1 Branch and bound diagram with optimal solution at node 4.

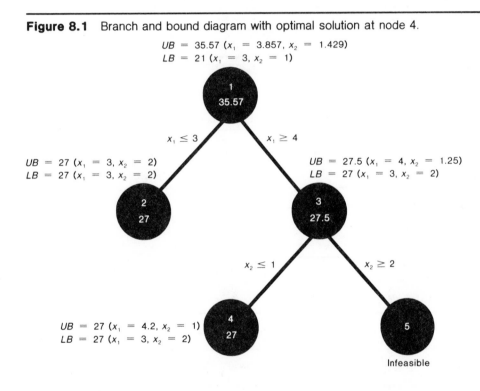

The variable $x_1 = 3.857$ has a larger fractional part than $x_2 = 1.429$, so we will branch on x_1. The new constraints are $x_1 \leq 3$ and $x_1 \geq 4$, which form nodes 2 and 3 in figure 8.1. To find the bounds at these nodes, relaxed solutions of the original problem, with each bounding constraint added in turn, must be found. These are shown in tables 8.2 and 8.3.

Table 8.2 Relaxed Solution at Node 2

c_j			5	6	0	0	0
	basic variable	quantity	x_1	x_2	s_1	s_2	s_3
6	x_2	2	0	1	1/3	0	−1/3
0	s_2	2	0	0	−4/3	1	−7/3
5	x_1	3	1	0	0	0	1
	z_j	27	5	6	2	0	3
	$c_j − z_j$		0	0	−2	0	−3

Table 8.3 Relaxed Solution at Node 3

c_i			5	6	0	0	0
	basic variable	quantity	x_1	x_2	s_1	s_2	s_3
0	s_1	.25	0	0	1	$-3/4$	$-7/4$
6	x_2	1.25	0	1	0	1/4	5/4
5	x_1	4	1	0	0	0	-1
	z_j	27.5	5	6	0	3/2	5/2
	$c_j - z_j$		0	0	0	$-3/2$	$-5/2$

We have now completed the steps of the branch and bound method through step 5. Since we have a new integer solution that is the existing maximum integer solution, 27 becomes the lower bound at nodes 2 and 3. Following step 7, we will next branch from node 3 with the two new constraints $x_2 \leq 1$ and $x_2 \geq 2$. The relaxed solutions at nodes 4 and 5 are shown in tables 8.4 and 8.5.

Table 8.4 Relaxed Solution at Node 4

c_i			5	6	0	0	0	0
	basic variable	quantity	x_1	x_2	s_1	s_2	s_3	s_4
0	s_1	.6	0	0	1	$-2/5$	0	-1
0	s_3	.2	0	0	0	1/5	1	-1
5	x_1	4.2	1	0	0	1/5	0	-1
6	x_2	1	0	1	0	0	0	1
	z_j	27	5	6	0	1	0	1
	$c_j - z_j$		0	0	0	-1	0	-1

Table 8.5 Relaxed Solution at Node 5

c_i			5	6	0	0	0	0	$-M$	$-M$
	basic variable	quantity	x_1	x_2	s_1	s_2	s_3	s_4	A_1	A_2
5	x_1	27/7	1	0	$-4/7$	3/7	0	0	0	0
$-M$	A_1	4/7	0	0	$-5/7$	2/7	0	-1	0	1
$-M$	A_2	1/7	0	0	$-4/7$	$-3/7$	-1	0	1	0
6	x_2	10/7	0	1	5/7	$-2/7$	0	0	0	0
	z_j		5	6	$\frac{10}{7}+\frac{9M}{7}$	$\frac{3}{7}+\frac{M}{7}$	M	M	$-M$	$-M$
	$c_j - z_j$		0	0	$-\frac{10}{7}-\frac{9M}{7}$	$-\frac{3}{7}-\frac{M}{7}$	$-M$	$-M$	0	0

The relaxed solution at node 5 is infeasible. At node 4 the upper and lower bounds are the same, which means that there is an integer solution with the greatest upper bound value. The optimal solution has been found at $x_1 = 3$, $x_2 = 2$, and $Z = 27$.

Case *Massachusetts Metals*

"Of course, Jim, I know you'll plan this production in such a way that the total production cost will be as low as possible. Let me know what you decide to do." With these words, Don O'Rourke, production vice president of Massachusetts Metals, closed his conversation with Jim Danielson, the company's production scheduler. Massachusetts Metals had just contracted to do stamping on 3,000 castings, and Danielson was to schedule the work.

The purchase of two new machines had complicated Jim's job. In the past, all stamping had been done on one machine. Now, with the delivery of the two new machines, Jim had to find some way to decide how much stamping would be done on each machine. None of the machines could handle the entire 3,000 unit order, and there were different costs to set up and run each machine, as shown in exhibit 8.1.

Exhibit 8.1 Cost and Capacity Information

Machine	Set-Up Cost (Fixed)	Unit Cost (Variable)	Maximum Capacity
1	200	30	1,000
2	500	5	1,200
3	350	10	1,800

To Jim, this seemed like a mathematical programming problem. He realized that he would need two kinds of integer variables. The first kind would tell how many units would be stamped on each of the three machines. The second type of integer variable would be a set of 0 — 1 variables to "turn on" or "turn off" a machine, to be sure that the capacity of the machine was not available unless the set-up cost had been incurred.

What should the production schedule be?

9 Goal Programming

Key Concepts

I. Definition of *goal programming*
   A. Goal programming is the application of linear programming techniques to problems with more than one objective (goal) to be satisfied.
   B. Goal programming obtains a solution in which *deviations from goals* are minimized.

II. Formulating the goal programming model
   A. First formulate the problem as a linear programming problem without regard to goals.
   B. Next specify the goals or objectives in the order (*priority*) they should be met.
   C. Rewrite each linear programming constraint as a *goal constraint* in which the deviations from the goal are expressed as *deviational variables*.
   D. Write the new objective function to minimize each deviational variable at its appropriate priority level and weight.

III. Solve the two-variable goal programming problem graphically.
   A. Plot each goal constraint, assuming the deviational variables are zero.
   B. Beginning with the priority one goal, successively minimize each deviational variable by setting it equal to zero and eliminate the corresponding area from the graph.
   C. Continue until all goals have been met, indicating that the graphical solution is *optimal,* or until the graphical solution becomes infeasible, meaning that not all goals can be achieved. The best graphical solution to the latter situation in which all higher priority goals are achieved is called a *satisfactory* solution.

IV. Use the *modified simplex* method to solve goal programming problems.
   A. Using the final goal programming formulation of the problem, set up the initial simplex tableau. Compute the $z_j - P_j$ rows to satisfy the priority one goal first.
   B. Perform the usual simplex pivot operations using the pivot criteria of meeting the highest priority goal that has not been attained.
   C. Continue the simplex until the most satisfactory solution is obtained that would not violate any higher level goal.

V. Applications of goal programming
   A. Goal programming may be applied in situations in which there is more than one objective.
   B. It is especially applicable for nonbusiness organizations whose objectives are not primarily to maximize profit but rather to meet other specific criteria.
   C. Goal programming can assist the manager in performing sensitivity analysis, where fixed constraints are restated as goal constraints.

Quiz

True-False

T F 1. Goal programming might be useful when the linear programming solution to a problem is infeasible.

T F 2. The functions in goal programming may be nonlinear or linear.

T F 3. At least one or both deviational variables in a goal constraint must equal zero.

T F 4. If we have overutilization of resource number 1, d_1^- will be positive.

T F 5. It is possible in goal programming to have a goal constraint allowing deviation either only above or only below the resource.

T F 6. P_4 implies a higher level of importance than P_2.

T F 7. Goal programming may be applied in situations in which there is more than one objective.

Short Answer

8. Describe the differences between an optimal solution and a satisfactory solution. Can a goal programming solution also be "optimal"?

9. Discuss how the modified simplex method differs from the regular simplex method.

10. Explain why it is possible (and sometimes desirable) to have two or more objective functions at the same priority level.

11. Why is goal programming especially useful for nonbusiness organizations?

Problems

1. The administrator of Metropolitan Hospital is reviewing several departmental requests concerning a proposed new wing. At issue is the number of beds for each department.

Dept	No. of Beds Requested	Cost Per Bed	Area Per Bed (sq. ft.)	Annual No. of Patients/Bed
A	50	$ 4,000	200	35
B	30	8,000	500	90
C	20	10,000	700	10

The new wing is currently planned for 30,000 square feet.
The hospital board has established the following prioritized goals:
a. Try to avoid spending more than $550,000.
b. At least 4,000 patients should be served annually in the new wing.
c. Avoid a plan that uses more than 30,000 square feet.
d. Try to meet the departmental requests for the number of beds requested. However, this goal should be weighted in proportion to the annual number of patients served per bed.

Formulate a goal programming model to determine the number of each type of bed to include in the new wing in order to best achieve the board's goals.

Solution

We can first write the problem as a cost minimization linear programming problem. Let x_1, x_2, and x_3 be the number of beds for departments A, B, and C respectively.

$$\text{minimize } Z = \$4,000x_1 + \$8,000x_2 + \$10,000x_3$$
subject to
$$200x_1 + 500x_2 + 700x_3 \leq 30,000 \text{ square feet}$$
$$35x_1 + 90x_2 + 10x_3 \geq 4,000 \text{ patients}$$
$$x_1 \leq 50 \text{ beds}$$
$$x_2 \leq 30 \text{ beds}$$
$$x_3 \leq 20 \text{ beds}$$
$$x_1, x_2, x_3 \geq 0$$

Cost Goal

The objective function can be restated as a goal constraint, using $550,000 as the maximum cost:

$$4,000x_1 + 8,000x_2 + 10,000x_3 + d_1^- - d_1^+ = \$550,000$$

In this constraint, d_1^- represents the amount spent *below* $550,000, while d_1^+ represents the amount spent in excess of $550,000. The new objective function will be:

$$\text{minimize } P_1 d_1^+$$

Notice that d_1^- does not appear in the objective function since we are not concerned with spending less than $550,000. P_1 indicates that this goal has first priority.

Patients Served Goal

Since the second priority goal is to serve at least 4,000 patients, this goal constraint is:

$$35x_1 + 90x_2 + 10x_3 + d_2^- - d_2^+ = 4{,}000 \text{ patients}$$

The deviation variables d_2^- and d_2^+ represent the annual number of patients served below and above 4,000 respectively. The new objective function reflects this second priority goal:

$$\text{minimize } P_1 d_1^+, \; P_2 d_2^-$$

Since this goal is primarily concerned with serving no fewer than 4,000 patients, d_2^+ does not appear in the objective function.

Area Goal

The 30,000 square foot goal can be expressed as:

$$200x_1 + 500x_2 + 700x_3 + d_3^- - d_3^+ = 30{,}000 \text{ square feet}$$

where d_3^- is the number of unused square feet below 30,000 and d_3^+ is the excess number of square feet above 30,000. The objective function should be updated as:

$$\text{minimize } P_1 d_1^+, \; P_2 d_2^-, \; P_3 d_3^+$$

Departmental Request Goal

In order to meet the departmental requests, the following goal constraints are formulated:

$$x_1 + d_4^- = 50 \text{ beds}$$
$$x_2 + d_5^- = 30 \text{ beds}$$
$$x_3 + d_6^- = 20 \text{ beds}$$

Since each department has requested the maximum number of beds it will need, no deviational variables dealing with allocating more than the request are included. The objective function can be written as:

$$\text{maximize } P_1 d_1^+, \; P_2 d_2^-, \; P_3 d_3^+, \; 35 P_4 d_4^- + 90 P_4 d_5^- + 10 P_4 d_6^-$$

Notice that all three departmental requests are considered at the same priority level (P_4), but they are weighted in proportion to the number of patients served per bed. Since department B serves the most patients per bed (90), its request is the most important at this priority. The other two departmental requests are less important, yet still considered at this level.

The final goal programming model is:

$$\text{minimize } P_1 d_1^+, \; P_2 d_2^-, \; P_3 d_3^+, \; 35 P_4 d_4^- + 90 P_4 d_5^- + 10 P_4 d_6^-$$
subject to
$$4{,}000x_1 + 8{,}000x_2 + 10{,}000x_3 + d_1^- - d_1^+ = 550{,}000$$
$$35x_1 + 90x_2 + 10x_3 + d_2^- - d_2^+ = 4{,}000$$
$$200x_1 + 500x_2 + 700x_3 + d_3^- - d_3^+ = 30{,}000$$
$$x_1 + d_4^- = 50$$
$$x_2 + d_5^- = 30$$
$$x_3 + d_6^- = 20$$
$$x_1, x_2, x_3, d_1^-, d_1^+, d_2^-, d_2^+, d_3^-, d_3^+, d_4^-, d_5^-, d_6^- \geq 0$$

2. Solve the following goal programming problem using the modified simplex method.

$$\text{minimize } P_1 d_1^-, \; 1 P_2 d_2^- + 2 P_2 d_3^-, \; P_3 d_4^+$$
subject to
$$4x_1 + 3x_2 + d_1^- - d_1^+ = 500$$
$$x_1 + d_2^- = 50$$
$$x_2 + d_3^- = 75$$
$$x_1 + 2x_2 + d_4^- - d_4^+ = 120$$
$$x_1, x_2, d_1^-, d_1^+, d_2^-, d_3^-, d_4^-, d_4^+ \geq 0$$

Solution

Create the initial tableau as shown in table 9.1. The initial basis is composed of d_1^-, d_2^-, d_3^-, and d_4^-. The largest coefficient of P_1 in the $z_j - P_j$ rows is 4; thus, x_1 should enter the solution. The minimum positive quantity/pivot column ratio is 50, indicating that d_2^- leaves the basis.

The method continues through tables 9.2, 9.3, and 9.4 until only the P_3 coefficients are positive in the $z_j - P_j$ rows. Since the higher priority goals are already satisfied, attempting to satisfy the third priority goal will lead to a *less satisfactory* solution. Thus the solution from table 9.4 is the most satisfactory solution.

Table 9.1 Tableau 1

P_j	basic variables	quantity	x_1	x_2	P_1 d_1^-	$1P_2$ d_2^-	$2P_2$ d_3^-	d_4^-	P_3 d_1^+	d_4^+	
P_1	d_1^-	500	4	3	1	0	0	0	-1	0	$500/4 = 125$
P_2	d_2^-	50	1	0	0	1	0	0	0	0	$50/1 = 50 \leftarrow$ Pivot Row
$2P_2$	d_3^-	75	0	1	0	0	1	0	0	0	$75/0 = \infty$
	d_4^-	120	1	2	0	0	0	1	0	-1	$120/1 = 120$
	P_3	0	0	0	0	0	0	0	0	$-P_3$	
$z_j - P_j$	P_2	$200P_2$	P_2	$2P_2$	0	0	0	0	0	0	
	P_1	$500P_1$	$4P_1$	$3P_1$	0	0	0	0	$-P_1$	0	

Pivot Column (under x_1)

Table 9.2. Tableau 2

P_j	basic variables	quantity	x_1	x_2	P_1 d_1^-	$1P_2$ d_2^-	$2P_2$ d_3^-	d_4^-	P_3 d_1^+	d_4^+	
P_1	d_1^-	300	0	3	1	-4	0	0	-1	0	$300/3 = 100$
	x_1	50	1	0	0	1	0	0	0	0	$50/0 = \infty$
$2P_2$	d_3^-	75	0	1	0	0	1	0	0	0	$75/1 = 75$
	d_4^-	70	0	2	0	-1	0	1	0	-1	$70/2 = 35 \leftarrow$ Pivot Row
	P_3	0	0	0	0	0	0	0	0	$-P_3$	
$z_j - P_j$	P_2	$150P_2$	0	$2P_2$	0	$-P_2$	0	0	0	0	
	P_1	$300P_1$	0	$3P_1$	0	$-4P_1$	0	0	$-P_1$	0	

Pivot Column (under x_2)

Table 9.3. Tableau 3

P_j	basic variables	quantity	x_1	x_2	P_1 d_1^-	$1P_2$ d_2^-	$2P_2$ d_3^-	d_4^-	P_3 d_1^+	d_4^+	
P_1	d_1^-	195	0	0	1	$-5/2$	0	$-3/2$	-1	$3/2$	$195/\dfrac{3}{2} = 130$
	x_1	50	1	0	0	1	0	0	0	0	$50/0 = \infty$
$2P_2$	d_3^-	40	0	0	0	$1/2$	1	$-1/2$	0	$1/2$	$40/1/2 = 80 \leftarrow$ Pivot Row
	x_2	35	0	1	0	$-1/2$	0	$1/2$	0	$-1/2$	negative
	P_3	0	0	0	0	0	0	0	0	$-P_3$	
$z_j - P_j$	P_2	$80P_2$	0	0	0	0	0	$-P_2$	0	P_2	
	P_1	$195P_1$	0	0	0	$-7/2P_1$	0	$-3/2P_1$	$-P_1$	$3/2P_1$	

Pivot Column (under d_4^+)

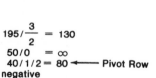

Goal Programming

Table 9.4. The Optimal Modified Simplex Tableau

P_j					P_1	$1P_2$	$2P_2$			P_3
	basic variables		quantity	x_1	x_2	d_1^-	d_2^-	d_3^-	d_4^-	d_1^+	d_4^+
P_1	d_1^-		75	0	0	1	-4	-3	0	-1	0
	x_1		50	1	0	0	1	0	0	0	0
P_3	d_4^+		80	0	0	0	1	2	-1	0	1
	x_2		75	0	1	0	0	1	0	0	0
	P_3		$80P_3$	0	0	0	P_3	$2P_3$	$-P_3$	0	0
$z_j - P_j$	P_2		0	0	0	0	$-P_2$	$-2P_2$	0	0	0
	P_1		$75P_1$	0	0	0	$-4P_1$	$-3P_1$	0	$-P_1$	0

Final Solution:

$x_1 = 50$ $d_1^- = 75$ $d_1^+ = 0$ $d_3^- = 0$

$x_2 = 75$ $d_4^+ = 80$ $d_2^- = 0$ $d_4^- = 0$

Objective Function: $75P_1 + 80P_3$

Case   *Pan Global Airlines*

Pan Global Airlines (PGA) was faced with three possible route expansion alternatives under the airline deregulation program. They had to consider the impact on profitability, aircraft fleet utilization, cabin attendant availability, and flight crew hours. Exhibit 9.1 illustrates some of the market and flight data for the routes.

Joe Zink had been assigned the job of assembling the data and making a preliminary recommendation to the PGA vice-president on the number of trips per route to schedule. Zink knew that although the aircraft on route A has 100 seats, the 75% load factor meant that the plane usually had only 75 seats occupied on trips of that kind, so he changed the capacity to 75. The operations department advised him to use 16 trips per week as an average for cabin attendants, regardless of which route or aircraft they were assigned to. However, flight crew hours were limited by law to 16 hours per week per crew member, regardless of aircraft type. After checking with crew schedulers, Joe found that 75 cabin attendants and 75 flight crew members were available for the new routes. He wondered whether PGA had enough crew resources to make all the flights.

Aircraft availability was a different situation. Zink knew that each route required a different type of airplane. He had already changed the seat capacities to realistically reflect the load factors expected in each route. Due to maintenance and networking requirements with other PGA routes, aircraft available for route A were limited to a total of 90 trips per week while aircraft available for routes B and C were limited to 60 and 15 weekly trips, respectively.

Zink decided to use linear programming on the PGA computer system to determine the optimal number of trips to schedule on routes A, B, and C, assuming no additional personnel or aircraft would be available.

A quick glance at the output showed that the resources available for these routes were not balanced— he had excess personnel and planes on some routes, and shortages on others. Zink decided to establish PGA's priorities for the resource utilization and profit ability goals for the new routes.

1. If possible, PGA did not want to divert any additional aircraft to the new routes.
2. Avoid using more flight crew personnel than the 75 already available.
3. The new route allocation should provide a minimum profit of $600,000 per week.
4. PGA should carry at least as many passengers as possible, but not to exceed the market estimates indicated. However, this goal should be weighted in proportion to the *size* of the market on each route.
5. Avoid using more than 75 cabin attendants.

Zink knew that any unassigned flight crew or cabin crew members could be used on other routes, as could any unassigned aircraft.

He decided to formulate a goal programming model to handle the priorities for the various goals.

Exhibit 9.1 Market and Flight Characteristics for Route Expansion Alternatives

Route	Maximum No. of Seats Per Week	Net Profit Per Seat	Cabin Attendants Per Trip	Flight Crew Hours Per Trip	Maximum Seats Per Aircraft	Average Load Factor
A	7,200	$40	4	6.0	100	.75
B	4,600	55	7	9.0	140	.60
C	2,500	80	10	13.5	250	.52

10 Probability

Key Concepts

I. The concepts studied so far have been deterministic (all facts have been known with certainty) but now we must study the basics of probability to be able to make decisions under uncertainty.
   A. Objective probability is determined mathematically according to some rule.
      1. *Classical probability* measures the ratio of the number of things we want to happen to the total number of things that can happen.
      2. Probabilities based on *relative frequency* measure what proportion of time an event has happened in the past.
   B. *Subjective probabilities* are "best guesses" about the likelihood of an event and are usually estimated by people with some expertise in the area.

II. Probability is a number between zero and one and is associated with an event.
   A. The probabilities of all possible events must add up to 1.00.
   B. *Mutually exclusive events* are those with nothing in common; an item can only belong to one of the events.
   C. When events are *collectively exhaustive,* it means that every item is a member of an event.
   D. The probability that one event or another will occur is equal to the marginal probability of the first event plus the marginal probability of the second event minus their joint probability, or

$$P(A \text{ or } B) = P(A) + P(B) - P(AB)$$

III. *Independent events* do not give information about each other, but dependent events do, allowing probabilities to be revised.
   A. If A and B are *dependent events,* then the probability that A will happen, given we know B has happened, is

$$P(A \mid B) = \frac{P(AB)}{P(B)}$$

   B. If A and B are independent, then

$$P(A \mid B) = P(A) \text{ and } P(AB) = P(A) \cdot P(B)$$

   (Remember, only true when A and B are independent.)
   C. The relationship between events and the marginal, joint, and conditional probabilities associated with those events conveniently can be shown on a probability tree diagram.
   D. *Bayes' Rule* allows us to calculate conditional probabilities (often we need the "reverse" of what we have) by the formula
$$P(A \mid C) = \frac{P(C \mid A)P(A)}{P(C \mid A)P(A) + P(C \mid B)P(B)}$$

IV. *Random variables* are variables in which every value of the variable has a probability associated with it.
   A. The *expected value* of a random variable is found by multiplying each value of the random variable by its probability and then summing up all these products, or

$$E(x) = \sum_{i=1}^{n} x_i P(x_i)$$

B. The *variance* of a random variable is found by subtracting the expected value from each value of the random variable, squaring each difference, multiplying by the respective probabilities and then adding up the terms:

$$\sigma^2 = \sum_{i=1}^{n} [x_i - E(x)]^2 P(x_i)$$

C. The *standard deviation* is found by taking the square root of the variance.
D. Random variables with certain properties follow special probability distributions.
    1. If there are two possible outcomes of each trial, the probabilities of the outcomes remain the same over time, the outcomes are independent, and the number of trials is discrete and integer, we are dealing with the *binomial distribution*.
        a. The random variable is the number of successes (r) in a specific number (n) of trials.
        b. The probability of the random variable is given by

$$P(r) = \frac{n!}{r!\,(n-r)!} \, p^r \, (q)^{n-r}$$

    where
        p = probability of a success
        $q = 1-p$ = probability of a failure

    2. A continuous random variable whose frequency distribution follows a bell shape often fulfills the other, more technical, requirements to be *normally distributed*.
        a. Since the distribution is continuous, we cannot find the probability of any one specific point but must speak of the probability that the random variable takes on a value within some range.
        b. To find the probability, convert the problem to one using the standard normal probability:

$$Z = \frac{x - \mu}{\sigma}$$

    and then use the tabled probabilities for specific values of Z.

Quiz

Short Answer

1. Explain the difference between deterministic and probabilistic events and give examples of each.

2. Cable television viewers in a certain city receive two NBC stations, three CBS stations, two ABC stations, two PBS stations, one all sports station, one all news station, and one independent station. If the channel selector is turned at random, what is the (classical) probability it will stop on a CBS station? on an independent station? on a PBS station?

3. Course records show that the enrollment in a college computer science course is divided among 8 freshmen, 20 sophomores, 15 juniors, 5 seniors, and 2 graduate students. If a student is chosen at random from this class, what is the (relative frequency) probability that the student is a junior?

4. In order to understand subjective probability, ask five different people for their assessment of the chances that your school will win the first football game in the coming season.

5. Can a probability ever be larger than one?

6. Are the events in question three mutually exclusive? collectively exhaustive?

7. If $P(A) = .4$, $P(B) = .2$, and $P(A \text{ or } B) = .5$, then what is the joint probability of A and B?

8. In question 7, what is the marginal probability of B?

9. Are the events "A: draw a red card from a well shuffled deck of cards" and "B: draw a queen from a well shuffled deck of cards" independent events?

10. If there is another event "C: draw a heart from a well shuffled deck of cards," are A and C independent events? Are B and C independent events?

11. Draw a tree diagram representing three tosses of an unfair coin, which has $P(\text{Heads}) = 3/5$ and $P(\text{Tails}) = 2/5$.

12. Confirm that question 11 describes a binomial distribution problem by finding $P(2 \text{ heads})$ from your tree diagram and by the binomial formula.

13. Calculate 6!.

14. Given the random variable x and the associated probabilities, find $E(x)$.

x	0	1	2	3	4
$p(x)$	.2	.1	.2	.2	.3

15. Using the information in question 14, find the variance of x.

Problems

1. Clients of the consulting firm of Swingman and Hodge are classified as to whether they are new or repeat clients, and whether or not the case is completed within a month. Of 100 cases so far this year, 40 have been repeat customers from previous years. Of these 40, 30% have been completed within a month. A total of 38 cases took longer than a month to complete.
   a. Develop a joint probability table
   b. Develop a probability tree showing appropriate marginal, conditional, and joint probabilities.
   c. Using Bayes' Rule, find the probability a client was new if the case was solved in less than a month.

Solution

a. First set up a diagram such as table 10.1 that gives the classifications and totals, and fill in the numbers that are given. We know

   total clients $= 100$
   total repeat clients $= 40$
   repeat clients completed within month $= (30\%)40 = 12$
   total cases taking over a month $= 38$

   Of course, at this time the entries in the table are frequencies, not probabilities.

Table 10.1 Known Facts for Joint Frequency Table

	New Clients	Repeat Clients	Total
$\leq$ month		12	
$>$ month			38
Total		40	100

Next, fill in the blanks by making all of the rows and columns sum to the totals. See table 10.2.

Table 10.2 Joint Frequency Table

	New Clients	Repeat Clients	Total
$\leq$ month	50	12	62
$>$ month	10	28	38
Total	60	40	100

Finally, convert the frequency table to a probability table by dividing all entries by the total frequency of 100, as in table 10.3.

Table 10.3   Joint Probability Table

	New Clients	Repeat Clients	Total
≤ month	.5	.12	.62
> month	.1	.28	.38
Total	.6	.40	1.00

b. Since the firm knows whether the client is new or repeat before it knows how long it will take for the case to be completed, it makes sense for the first branch of the tree diagram to deal with new or repeat client. The tree diagram would be as shown in figure 10.1. To calculate the conditional probabilities, use your answers to part a.

$$P(\text{completed} \leq \text{month} \mid \text{new client}) = \frac{.5}{.6} = .83$$

$$P(\text{completed} \leq \text{month} \mid \text{repeat client}) = \frac{.12}{.4} = .3$$

Since immediately following each branch point of a tree diagram we have mutually exclusive and collectively exhaustive events, the remaining conditional probabilities can be found by simple subtraction from 1.00.

Figure 10.1   Tree diagram for problem 1.b.

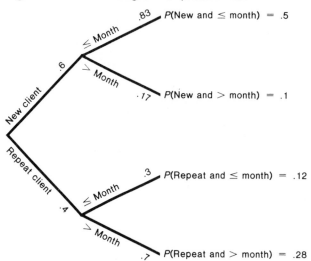

c. Using Bayes' Rule, we find

$P(\text{new client} \mid \text{completed} \leq \text{month})$

$$= \frac{P(\leq \text{month} \mid \text{new}) \, P(\text{new})}{P(\leq \text{month} \mid \text{new}) \, P(\text{new}) + P(\leq \text{month} \mid \text{repeat}) \, P(\text{repeat})}$$

$$= \frac{(.83)(.6)}{(.83)(.6) + (.3)(.4)} = \frac{.5}{.62} = .81$$

Note: Some students find it simpler to use the multiplication already done for the joint probabilities on the decision tree to directly solve Bayes' Rule type problems rather than to write each specific step of Bayes' Rule.

2. Past sales figures for concessions at home basketball games for an NBA team show the average nightly sales to be $10,000 with standard deviation $2,500. If we assume sales are normally distributed, find the probability a night's sales will be:
   a. Over $12,000
   b. Between $5,000 and $15,000
   c. Under $14,000

Solution

It is always wise, when dealing with the normal distribution, to first sketch the normal curve, locate the mean, and shade the area under consideration.

a. $P(x > 12000)$

   Converting the probability in terms of x (dollars) to Z, we have

$$P(x > 12000) = P\left(Z > \frac{12000 - 10000}{2500}\right) = P(Z > .8)$$

The probability for $Z = .8$ is .2881. However, this is the area between the mean and our point, so we must subtract to get $.5 - .2881 = .2119$.

Figure 10.2 Normal curve showing area for 2.a.

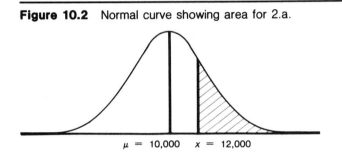

$\mu = 10,000$ $x = 12,000$

b. $P(5000 < x < 15000)$

   Converting to the Z scale we have:

$$P(5000 < x < 15000) = P\left(\frac{5000 - 10000}{2500} < Z < \frac{15000 - 10000}{2500}\right)$$

$$= P(-2 < Z < 2) = .4772 + .4772 = .9544$$

Note: The negative Z value simply indicates a value to the left of the mean. Remember that probability cannot be negative.

Figure 10.3 Normal curve showing area for 2.b.

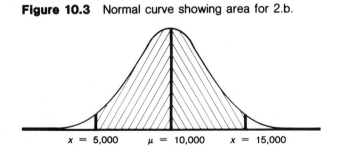

$x = 5,000$ $\mu = 10,000$ $x = 15,000$

c. $P(x < 14000)$
Converting to the Z scale we have:

$$P(x < 14000) = P\left(Z < \frac{14000 - 10000}{2500}\right)$$

$$= P(Z < 1.6) = .5 + .4452 = .9452.$$

Figure 10.4 Normal curve showing area for 2.c.

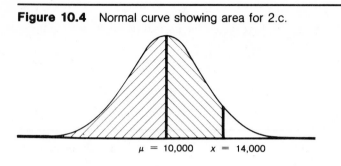

$\mu = 10,000$ $x = 14,000$

11 Decision Analysis

Key Concepts

I. Decision making under conditions of uncertainty may be classified as to whether probabilities can or cannot be assigned to the future outcomes.
  A. To make decisions when probabilities are unknown, the *payoff* for every *decision* and *state of nature* pair must be created.
    1. The *maximax criterion* has the decision maker select the decision that will contain the maximum of the maximum payoffs.
    2. The *maximin criterion* has the decision maker select the decision that will contain the maximum of the minimum payoffs.
    3. The *minimax regret criterion* has the decision maker create a regret table and then choose the decision that will contain the minimum of the maximum regrets.
    4. The *Hurwicz criterion* requires the decision maker to decide on a coefficient of optimism (α) and then, for each decision, multiply the maximum payoff by α and the minimum payoff by $(1 - \alpha)$, sum these, and choose the decision with the highest sum.
    5. The *equal likelihood criterion* weights each state of nature equally, multiplies payoffs by weights for each state and chooses the decision with the largest sum.
  B. When probabilities exist, they can be used with a payoff or regret table or a decision tree to indicate the best course of action.
    1. Under the *expected value criterion*, the payoff of each outcome is multiplied by the probability of its occurrence, the products are summed, and the decision with the highest expected value is selected.
    2. Under the *expected opportunity cost*, the regret table instead of the payoff table is used, and the decision with the lowest expected value is selected.
II. A number of quantities and techniques exist to aid decision makers when probabilities are present.
  A. The *expected value of perfect information, EVPI,* is given by the expected value *given* perfect information minus the expected value *without* information; this quantity is also equal to the *expected opportunity loss* of the optimal decision.
  B. *Decision trees* can graphically describe a problem.
    1. Decisions and states of nature are both reflected in decision trees; decision nodes are boxes and the following branches have no probabilities, and state of nature nodes are circles and the following branches do have probabilities.
    2. Trees are usually laid out in chronological order.
    3. Decision trees become more useful than payoff tables when sequential decisions exist.
    4. To decide on a decision strategy from a tree, start at the end of the tree and find the expected values at state of nature nodes; at decision nodes, choose the branch with the largest expected value, "pruning" off all others, to continue going backward through the tree, subtracting decision costs where appropriate.
  C. Many decision problems allow us to make use of sample information, which revises prior probabilities to posterior probabilities using Bayes' Rule.
    1. A decision tree that reflects the possible outcomes of sample information must be drawn.
    2. Careful thought must be given to what conditional probabilities are needed, and then Bayes' Rule will usually be needed to calculate them.
    3. The best decision strategy is then found by using expected value.
    4. The *expected value of sample information, EVSI,* is given by the expected value *with* sample information minus the expected value with *no* information. For the information to be worthwhile, the cost of the sample information should be less than the EVSI.
    5. *Efficiency* of information is the ratio of EVSI to EVPI.

D. A decision maker's attitude about different amounts of money and risk are reflected by using the decision criterion of *utility*.
   1. Utility values, based on individual preference, are assigned to net payoffs, and then expected utility governs which decision is made.
   2. The purchase of insurance and the existence of gamblers are graphic examples of the existence of the utility criterion.

Quiz

Use the payoff table below to answer questions 1–10.

		States of Nature		
		1	2	3
	I	10	5	2
Decisions	II	3	8	5
	III	6	5	6

1. What decision should be made using maximax?
2. What decision should be made using maximin?
3. Construct the regret table.
4. What decision should be made using minimax regret?
5. What decision should be made using the Hurwicz criterion?
6. What decision should be made using equal likelihood?
7. If the probabilities of the states of nature are .2, .4, and .4, respectively, what decision should be made using expected value?
8. Given the same probabilities, find the expected opportunity loss for each decision.
9. What is the expected value *given* perfect information?
10. What is the EVPI?
11. What is the optimal decision strategy for the decision tree found in figure 11.1?

Figure 11.1 Tree diagram for question 11.

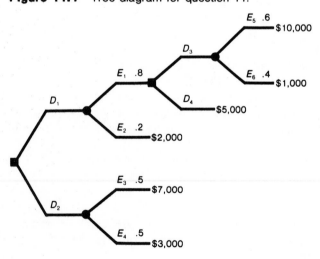

Decision Analysis

12. Use Bayes' Rule to complete the entries in table 11.1, where the states of nature are high, medium, and low demand and the sample information is favorable, noncommittal, or unfavorable.

Table 11.1 Computation of Posterior Probabilities

States of Nature	Prior Probabilities	Conditional Probabilities	Prior × Conditional	Posterior Probabilities
High	$P(H) = .2$	$P(F/H) = .8$		$P(H/F) =$
Medium	$P(M) = .4$	$P(F/M) = .3$		$P(M/F) =$
Low	$P(L) = .4$	$P(F/L) = .1$		$P(L/F) =$
			$P(F) =$	
High		$P(N/H) = .1$		$P(H/N) =$
Medium		$P(N/M) = .5$		$P(M/N) =$
Low		$P(N/L) = .2$		$P(L/N) =$
			$P(N) =$	
High		$P(U/H) = .1$		$P(H/U) =$
Medium		$P(U/M) = .2$		$P(M/U) =$
Low		$P(U/L) = .7$		$P(L/U) =$
			$P(U) =$	

Problems

1. A company knows that demand for its product will be either 100, 200, or 300 units, so it must decide whether to stock 100, 200, or 300 units. Selling price per unit is $1.00, production cost per unit is $.40, and each unit made but not sold can be scrapped to recover $.10.
   a. How many units should be produced using the maximin criterion?
   b. How many units should be produced using the minimax regret criterion?

Solution

a. First, the payoff table must be constructed. There are three decisions and three states of nature. It is probably easiest to figure payoff by subtracting total cost from total revenue for each cell. These are entered in table 11.2.

Table 11.2 Payoff Table

		Demand		
		100	200	300
Supply	100	100−40= 60	100−40= 60	100−40= 60
	200	100−80+10= 30	200−80= 120	200−80= 120
	300	100−120+20= 0	200−120+10= 90	300−120= 180

For the maximin criterion, we must locate the minimum payoff for each decision.

Decision	Minimum Payoff
Supply 100	60
Supply 200	30
Supply 300	0

The decision to supply only 100 units contains the maximum of the minimum payoffs, so under maximin, we would decide to supply 100 units.

b. The regret table must be constructed. Choose the highest payoff in each column to have zero regret, and subtract the other entries in the column to calculate regret, as shown in table 11.3.

Table 11.3 Regret Table

| | | | Demand | |
		100	200	300
	100	0	60	120
Supply	200	30	0	60
	300	60	30	0

For the minimax regret criterion, we must locate the maximum regret for each decision.

Decision	Maximum Regret
Supply 100	120
Supply 200	60
Supply 300	60

Here, we have a tie. As far as the minimax regret criterion is concerned, we are indifferent between supplying 200 or 300 units. Another procedure, or common sense, could be used to resolve the tie.

2. A city is trying to decide whether or not to build a domed stadium in hopes of attracting a National Football League expansion team. They have been told that without a stadium, their chances of a franchise are non-existent.

The stadium will cost $60 million to build. Evaluating revenues on a fifteen-year horizon, it is estimated that the present value of revenue from a franchise and other off-season uses is $100 million. If the franchise is not awarded, then other uses should raise only $48 million. City planners estimate the chances at 40% that the franchise will be awarded.

It is possible to hire a consulting firm to give a favorable or unfavorable prediction for the franchise award. In similar situations, the firm has given a favorable report when the franchise was later awarded 75% of the time. It has given an unfavorable report when the franchise was later rejected 60% of the time.

What should the city do?

Solution

The first step is to draw the decision tree. In chronological order, we will have to do the following.
a. Decide whether or not to hire consultants.
b. If hired, get their report.
c. Decide whether or not to build stadium.
d. Find out about franchise.

The decision tree is shown in figure 11.2, with the appropriate dollar amounts shown.

Figure 11.2 Tree diagram for problem 2 (dollars in millions).

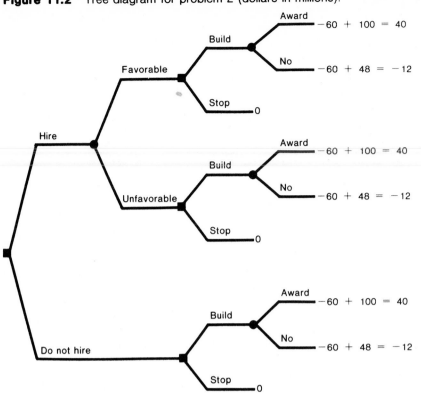

We know the probabilities:

$P(\text{award}) = .40$ $P(\text{no award}) = .60$
$P(\text{favorable} \mid \text{award}) = .75$ $P(\text{unfavorable} \mid \text{award}) = .25$
$P(\text{unfavorable} \mid \text{no award}) = .60$ $P(\text{favorable} \mid \text{no award}) = .40$

But for the upper branch of the tree we need:

$P(\text{favorable})$ $P(\text{unfavorable})$
$P(\text{award} \mid \text{favorable})$ $P(\text{no award} \mid \text{favorable})$
$P(\text{award} \mid \text{unfavorable})$ $P(\text{no award} \mid \text{unfavorable})$

As a result we will use table 11.4.

Table 11.4 Computation of Posterior Probabilities

States of Nature	Prior Probabilities	Conditional Probabilities	Prior × Conditional	Posterior Probabilities
Award	$P(A) = .4$	$P(F \mid A) = .75$	$P(FA) = .3$	$P(A \mid F) = .56$
No Award	$P(NA) = .6$	$P(F \mid NA) = .4$	$\underline{P(F(NA)) = .24}$	$P(NA \mid F) = .44$
			$P(F) = .54$	
Award	$P(A) = .4$	$P(U \mid A) = .25$	$P(UA) = .1$	$P(A \mid U) = .22$
No Award	$P(NA) = .6$	$P(U \mid NA) = .6$	$\underline{P(U(NA)) = .36}$	$P(NA \mid U) = .78$
			$P(U) = .46$	

These probabilities enable us to complete the expected values on the decision tree and formulate a strategy.

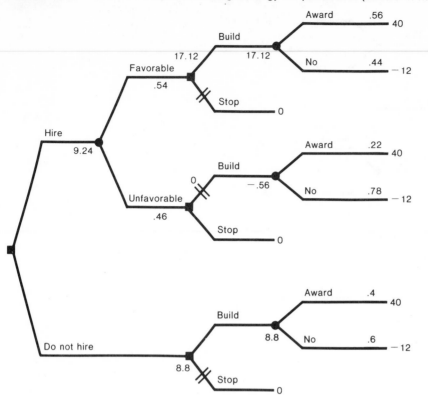

The best strategy for the city is to hire the consultants if their fee is significantly less then $440,000 = EVSI = 9,240,000 − 8,800,000. If the consultants give a favorable report, then the stadium should be built. If not, the stadium should not be built, based on this fifteen-year horizon.

___

Case   *The Golden Villa*

The Golden Pond is a fine restaurant located in the heart of a major midwestern city. The restaurant specializes in French and northern Italian cuisine and, since its opening ten years ago, has become one of the more popular places in town.

Mr. Michael Golden, proprietor, knows that much of the success of the Golden Pond is tied to other nearby attractions: the city's convention center, sports arenas, and theaters. For this reason, he is hesitant about launching the Golden Villa, a similar restaurant planned for the suburbs. Because of uncertainty as to how much his customers' preference for his cuisine is influenced by neighboring attractions, he estimates the chances for outstanding success, moderate success, or failure of the Golden Villa at .6, .25, and .15 respectively. The monetary figures for each of these levels of success are $50,000, $10,000, and −$40,000 (net profits based on a one-year horizon).

Although Mr. Golden trusts his own business sense, he is contemplating hiring, as consultant, a professor from the local university's school of restaurant and hotel management. Dr. Lynn Hayes has developed a survey with a good track record for predicting performance of other restaurant ventures. As Dr. Hayes had reported to Mr. Golden:

"My survey yields one of three outcomes, which we could call positive, so-so, and negative. Given those ventures that turned out to be outstanding successes, my survey said 'positive' 80% of the time, 'so-so' 15% of the time, and 'negative' only 5% of the time. When the venture was a moderate success, the respective percentages are 15%, 75%, and 10%, and when it was a failure the respective percentages are 0%, 30%, and 70%.

Mr. Golden was faced with a number of questions.

1. If he didn't hire Dr. Hayes, what should he do about opening the Golden Villa?
2. How much was her information worth, and what strategy should he follow if he did hire her?
3. How efficient was her information?

12 Game Theory

Key Concepts

I. The subject of *game theory* describes competitive decision making situations in which two or more decision makers compete to receive the best outcome.
   A. Games are classified on the basis of the number of players and in terms of the total of each player's gains and losses. We will study *two person, zero-sum games*.
   B. The monetary results of game strategies are placed in a payoff table, with the strategies of the player who is maximizing (the offensive player) along the left, and the strategies of the player who is minimizing (the defensive player) across the top.
II. The determination of the optimal strategy for a player depends on features of the game.
   A. When players adopt a single, *pure strategy* for the game, the offensive player selects the strategy with the largest of the minimum payoffs and the defensive player selects the strategy with the smallest of the maximum payoffs.
      1. A *dominant strategy* is one for which the payoffs are better than the payoffs for another strategy, and strategies that are dominated can be eliminated.
      2. The existence of an *equilibrium point* indicates the optimal strategy if pure strategies can be used.
   B. A *mixed strategy* occurs when each player selects an optimal strategy and they do not result in an equilibrium point.
      1. The expected gain and loss can be used to resolve the circular pattern of action and reaction in a mixed strategy game, by solving for the percentage of time each strategy should be employed.
      2. For problems with more than two strategies, linear programming can be used more easily than expected gain or loss.
         a. The objective is to optimize the value of the game.
         b. The constraints compare the expected value of the game to selected levels.

Quiz

True-False

T F   1. If a game player follows a pure strategy, he will always choose the same strategy.

T F   2. Rational individuals will always follow a pure strategy.

T F   3. Unless an equilibrium point exists, a pure strategy should not be followed.

T F   4. To determine an initial strategy the offensive player wants to choose the strategy that contains the maximum of the maximum payoffs.

T F   5. For his initial strategy the defensive player wants to choose the strategy that contains the minimum of the maximum payoffs.

Short Answer

6. Why is it important to look for dominant and dominated strategies?

7. Explain what makes a mixed strategy necessary.

8. A competitor has determined that he should choose strategy 1 70% of the time, so he always performs strategy 1 seven times in a row, then strategy 2 three times, and so forth. Is there any special advantage to being his opponent?

9. Why is it necessary to use linear programming in cases with more than two strategies?

10. What should be done if a game is to be played only once, and no equilibrium point exists?

Problems

1. Given the following payoff table for two individuals competing in a game, determine the optimal strategy for each player.

Table 12.1 Payoff Table

Individual I Strategies	Individual II Strategies		
	A	B	C
1	12	11	14
2	10	8	7
3	6	3	15

Solution

We can reduce the choices for Individual II by noticing that strategy B dominates strategy A. Strategy A has been eliminated in table 12.2.

Table 12.2 Payoff Table with Dominated Strategy Removed

Individual I Strategies	Individual II Strategies	
	B	C
1	11	14
2	8	7
3	3	15

Individual I first determines the minimum payoff for each strategy (11, 7, and 3) and chooses strategy 1 with the maximum minimum payoff.

Individual II selects strategy B after noticing that, of the maximum payoffs for each strategy, strategy B has a lower value (11) than strategy C (15).

Since 11 is an equilibrium point, if I and II are rational individuals, they will choose strategies 1 and B respectively.

2. Given the following mixed strategy game for two players, determine the initial strategy for each player and, using the expected gain and loss method, determine the mixed strategies for each player.

Table 12.3 Payoff Table

Player I Strategies	Player II Strategies	
	A	B
1	30	20
2	10	40

Solution

We should first confirm that there are no dominant strategies and that an equilibrium point does not exist.

Using the maximin and minimax rules, we see that player I would initially choose strategy 1 and player II would initially choose strategy A. But player II would see what player I did and choose B to save 10. But then player I would switch to strategy 2 to get 40. However, player II would soon go back to strategy A and a cycle would be set up.

Game Theory

To perform the expected gain and loss calculations, player I assumes that player II will choose strategy A, so player I will choose strategy 1 with probability p and strategy 2 with probability $1-p$. This gives an expected gain for player I, given player II selects A, of:

$$30p + 10(1-p) = 10 + 20p$$

If player II picks strategy B, the expected gain is:

$$20p + 40(1-p) = 40 - 20p$$

When these expected values are equated, we solve for p.

$$10 + 20p = 40 - 20p$$
$$40p = 30$$
$$p = .75$$

So player I should use strategy 1 75% of the time and strategy 2 25% of the time, and the expected gain is:

$$10 + 20(.75) = 10 + 15 = 25$$

For player II the procedure is the same. We equate:

$$30p + 20(1 - p) = 10p + 40(1 - p)$$
$$20 + 10p = 40 - 30p$$
$$40p = 20$$
$$p = .5$$

So player II should use each strategy half of the time. The expected loss is:

$$20 + 10(.5) = 25$$

as we found above.

Case *Hammer-Scissors-Paper*

The old children's game "Hammer-Scissors-Paper" is used to see which of two players will win and usually get his way on some important issue.

The game is played by having each player, on the count of three, hold out a hand. If the hand is a clenched fist, the sign is hammer. If two fingers are extended, the sign is scissors. If the palm is flat, the sign is paper. The hammer can smash (win over) the scissors, the scissors can cut (win over) the paper, but the paper can wrap up (win over) the hammer.

Analyze this game from the standpoint of a two person, zero-sum game. What sign would you recommend?

---

13 Markov Analysis

Key Concepts

I. *Markov analysis* provides probabilistic information on the status of a decision situation.
   A. Markov analysis is applicable to systems that exhibit probabilistic movement from one state or event to another, over time.
   B. The probability of moving from one state to another is called a *transition probability*.
   C. The set of all transition probabilities when expressed in matrix form is called the *transition matrix*.
   D. The transition matrix has certain properties or characteristics.
      1. The probabilities for a given beginning state of the system sum to 1.0.
      2. The probabilities apply to all participants in the system.
      3. The probabilities are constant over time.
      4. The states are independent over time.
II. Markov analysis can be used to determine the probability of being in a given state at some future time period.
   A. To find the probability of being in a given state after i periods in the future, successively multiply the transition matrix by itself i times.
   B. After a certain point in the future, the state probabilities may become constant. In other words, the probability of ending in a state after $i+1$ periods is the same as after i periods.
   C. If such a condition exists, the constant state probabilities are called *steady-state probabilities*. Certain transition matrices exhibit conditions for which special Markov analysis techniques are needed.
      1. *Absorbing state* matrices can "trap" a participant within a state.
      2. *Transient state* matrices can prevent a participant from returning to a state once it is reached.
      3. *Cyclic* matrices will cycle back and forth between several states without ever reaching steady-state.
III. Applications of Markov analysis involve using the state probabilities determined for some point in the future.
   A. Daily stock price movements may be predicted.
   B. Market shares may be predicted using the Markov brand switching approach.
   C. Car and truck rental firms can predict where their vehicles will be returned, a fact that can be used to determine drop-off charges for unpopular destinations.

Quiz

True-False

T F 1. The sum of the probabilities down each column in the transition matrix must be 1.0.

T F 2. Markov analysis will not give the optimal decision to make.

T F 3. Steady-state probabilities give the long-run likelihood of being in a given state regardless of starting state.

T F 4. At steady-state, the probabilities for all the states are equal.

T F 5. Once steady-state has been reached, the participants will remain in their current state and not switch.

T F 6. All transition matrices will reach steady-state at some point in the future.

T F 7. Markov analysis cannot be used unless the transition probabilities remain constant over time.

T F 8. In certain instances, decision trees can give us the same state probabilities that Markov analysis does.

T F   9. The steady-state probabilities also are the proportion of the population (participants) in each state.

T F   10. In the transition matrix, the sum of the probabilities for a given beginning state must be 1.0.

Exercises

11. Is the following matrix a valid transition matrix? Explain.

$$\begin{bmatrix} .3 & .4 & .3 \\ .2 & .8 & .1 \\ .4 & .2 & .4 \end{bmatrix}$$

12. Use the transition matrix below to determine the probability of being in state 2 next period given state 1 this period. What is the probability of being in state 2 in the third period given state 1 in the first period?

$$\begin{bmatrix} .43 & .57 \\ .62 & .38 \end{bmatrix}$$

13. Draw the decision tree diagram to illustrate the probabilities in exercise 12. Do your answers agree?

Problems

1. The new chicken sandwiches have been popular with many customers of fast-food restaurants. In fact, the local Big Burg restaurant is considering adding such an item. The only other fast-food restaurant in town, Burger Prince, already offers such a sandwich. The Markov transition probabilities for fast-food customers are:

| | Next Month | |
First Month	Big Burg (B)	Prince (P)
Big Burg (b)	.55	.45
Prince (p)	.30	.70

Calculate the steady-state probabilities for Big Burg (B) and Burger Prince (P). What percentage of the fast-food market will Big Burg have at steady-state?

Solution

Define $B_b(i)$ as the probability that a customer eats at Big Burg (B) in period i given that the customer originally ate at Big Burg (b). Likewise, $P_b(i)$ is the likelihood that a customer will eat at Burger Prince (P) in period i given that the customer originally ate at Big Burg (b).

Since at steady-state, the state probabilities for each state are constant:

$$[B_b(i)\ P_b(i)] = [B_b(i+1)\ P_b(i+1)] = [B_p P_b]$$

Thus we can write:

$$[B_b\ \ P_b] = [B_b P_b] \begin{bmatrix} .55 & .45 \\ .30 & .70 \end{bmatrix}$$

or

$$B_b = .55B_b + .30P_b$$
$$P_b = .45B_b + .70P_b$$

Since we know that $B_b + P_b = 1$, we can substitute $P_b = 1 - B_b$ into the first equation above.

$$B_b = .55B_b + .30 (1 - B_b)$$
$$= .55B_b + .30 - .30B_b$$

or combining terms:

$$B_b (1 - .55 + .30) = .30$$
$$\therefore B_b = .30/.75 = .40$$
$$\text{and } P_b = 1 - .40 = .60$$ steady-state probabilities

It appears that Big Burg will have about 40% of the customers while Burger Prince will get almost 60% of the market.

2. Suppose that Big Burg has hired a market research firm to estimate the transition probabilities if Big Burg were to introduce the chicken sandwich. This firm also estimated that the total fast-food market in the town is 5,000 customers per month, to be shared between the two restaurants.
The new transition matrix is:

First Month	Next Month	
	Big Burg (B)	Prince (P)
Big Burg (b)	.65	.35
Prince (p)	.40	.60

Calculate the new steady-state probabilities and estimate the number of monthly customers Big Burg should expect at steady-state.

Solution

Using the same approach as in problem 1, we can write the steady-state condition as:

$$[B_b \quad P_b] = [B_b \quad P_b] \begin{bmatrix} .65 & .35 \\ .40 & .60 \end{bmatrix}$$

or:

$$B_b = .65B_b + .40P_b$$
$$P_b = .35B_b + .60P_b$$

Substituting $P_b = 1 - B_b$ into the first equation:

$$B_b = .65B_b + .40(1 - B_b)$$

Solving for B_b:

$$B_b(1 - .65 + .40) = .40$$
$$B_b = .40/.75 = .533$$
$$P_b = 1 - .533 = .467$$ steady-state probabilities

Since Big Burg's steady-state market share is 53.3% of the estimated 5,000 customers, we can now predict that 2,665 customers will eat at Big Burg. Without the new chicken sandwich, Big Burg can only expect (.40) (5,000) = 2,000 customers per month.

Ross Associates was a financial research firm specializing in tracking daily stock price movements. Jane Ross had read in a recent financial magazine about using Markov analysis to determine transition and steady-state probabilities for stock price changes.

She decided to try that approach for a few stocks that her firm followed regularly. Using the computer terminal on her desk she was quickly able to call up on her screen the daily closing stock prices for the XYZ Corporation. Taking a representative period, she generated the hard-copy printout shown in exhibit 13.1.

She knew the three states in her Markov analysis were:

State 1:   stock price up from previous day
State 2:   stock price unchanged from previous day
State 3:   stock price down from previous day

Using the 60 closing prices, she decided to find out how many increased, decreased, or didn't change from the previous day, and then what happened to the price on the *following* day. Using the first four days as an example, on day 1 the price was 20 1/2 and on day 2 the price went up, so the first state is *up*. On day 3 the price was unchanged so she put a mark in the Up ⇒ Unchanged box in exhibit 13.2. On day 4 the price dropped, so Jane entered a mark in the cell corresponding to Unchanged ⇒ Down.

After calculating the cell frequencies for all 58 changes, she wondered what the transition probabilities would look like. To find the transition probabilities, Jane divided the 3 cell frequencies in each row by the sum of the cell frequencies for that row. Exhibit 13.3 shows similar sample calculations for a two-state transition matrix.

Now that Jane had the transition matrix, she wanted to find the steady-state probabilities for each state. She wondered if that would help explain why XYZ stock prices rose by more than $2 per share during the three-month period.

Exhibit 13.1   Daily Closing Stock Prices for XYZ Corporation (Read down each column)

XYZ Corporation
Daily Closing Stock Prices
January 1980–March 1980

20 1/2	20 1/2	25
21	20 1/2	23 1/2
21	20 1/4	23
20 1/4	20	23 1/4
20 3/8	20 1/8	24
21 3/8	20	24 1/8
22	19 7/8	24
21 7/8	19 1/2	23 1/2
21 1/2	20	24
21 7/8	20 3/8	23 7/8
21 7/8	20 7/8	24 1/4
22 3/8	20 1/2	25
22 1/4	20 7/8	24 1/2
22	21	23 7/8
21 1/2	20 5/8	22 1/2
21 3/8	21	23
21	21	23
20 3/4	21	23 1/2
21	22 1/2	22 7/8
20 3/4	24	22 5/8

Jane Ross, Analyst
1/23/81

Exhibit 13.2   Transition Frequencies for Stock Price Changes (Days 2–4)

	Next Day Price		
This Day Price	Up	Unchanged	Down
Up		/	
Unchanged			/
Down			

Exhibit 13.3   Sample Calculations for Two-State Transition Matrix

	Next Period		
This Period	State 1	State 2	
State 1	24	36	Σ = 60
State 2	17	15	Σ = 32

Cell Frequencies

	Next Period	
This Period	State 1	State 2
State 1	24/60	36/60
State 2	17/32	15/32

Transition Probabilities

14 Queuing Analysis

Key Concepts

I. *Queuing analysis* is a probabilistic method that can be used to predict the average *operating characteristics* of queuing (waiting line) systems.
   A. Probability of an empty system, P_o.
   B. Probability of n customers in the system, P_n.
   C. The average number of customers in the system, L.
   D. The average number of customers in the waiting line, L_q.
   E. The average time spent per customer in the system, W.
   F. The average time spent per customer in the waiting line, W_q.
   G. The utilization factor, P_u.
   H. The probability that the server is idle, I.
   I. The probability that a customer arriving in the system must wait for service, P_w.

II. The values for the operating characteristics depend on several factors.
   A. *Number of parallel servers* (serving a single queue)
      1. Single server
      2. Multiple servers
   B. The *queue discipline*
      1. First-come, first-served (most common)
      2. Last-come, first-served
      3. Other disciplines
   C. The *calling population* of arrivals
      1. Infinite source (most common)
      2. Finite source
   D. The *arrival rate,* or number of arrivals during a given time period.
      1. Poisson probability distribution
      2. Other distributions
   E. The *service time,* or time needed to service one customer.
      1. Exponential probability distribution
      2. Other distributions
   F. Other factors
      1. Balking (customer arrives but doesn't join the queue)
      2. Limited-capacity queues
      3. Reneging (customer leaves queue before being serviced)
      4. Jockeying (customer moves between queues)
      5. Several servers in sequence

III. The single server model
   A. Assumptions
      1. Infinite calling population
      2. First-come, first-served queue discipline
      3. Poisson arrival rate, mean $= a$
      4. Exponential service time at the single server, mean $= \dfrac{1}{s}$
      5. $a < s$ (arrival rate less than service rate)
   B. Operating characteristics
      1. $P_o = 1 - \dfrac{a}{s}$

2. $P_n = \left(\dfrac{a}{s}\right)^n \left(1 - \dfrac{a}{s}\right)$

3. $L = \dfrac{a}{s-a}$

4. $L_q = \dfrac{a^2}{s(s-a)} = L\left(\dfrac{a}{s}\right)$

5. $W = \dfrac{1}{s-a} = \dfrac{L}{a}$

6. $W_q = \dfrac{a}{s(s-a)} = W\left(\dfrac{a}{s}\right)$

7. $P_u = \dfrac{a}{s}$

8. $I = 1 - \dfrac{a}{s} = P_o$

9. $P_w = P_u = \dfrac{a}{s}$

IV. The multiple server model
  A. Assumptions
      1. Several (c) parallel servers serving a single queue
      2. Infinite calling population
      3. First-come, first-served queue discipline
      4. Poisson arrival rate, mean $= a$
      5. Exponential service time at each server, mean $= \dfrac{1}{s}$
      6. $a < cs$ (arrival rate less than combined service rate)
  B. Operating characteristics

1. $P_o = \dfrac{1}{\left[\displaystyle\sum_{n=0}^{c-1} \dfrac{1}{n!}\left(\dfrac{a}{s}\right)^n\right] + \dfrac{1}{c!}\left(\dfrac{a}{s}\right)^c\left(\dfrac{cs}{cs-a}\right)}$

2. $P_n = \dfrac{1}{c!\,c^{n-c}}\left(\dfrac{a}{s}\right)^n P_o$ for $n > c$

   $P_n = \dfrac{1}{n!}\left(\dfrac{a}{s}\right)^n P_o$ for $n \le c$

3. $L = \dfrac{as\left(\dfrac{a}{s}\right)^c}{(c-1)!\,(cs-a)^2}\,P_o + \dfrac{a}{s}$

4. $L_q = L - \dfrac{a}{s}$

5. $W = \dfrac{L}{a}$

6. $W_q = W - \dfrac{1}{s} = \dfrac{L_q}{a}$

7. $P_w = \dfrac{1}{c!}\left(\dfrac{a}{s}\right)^c\left(\dfrac{cs}{cs-a}\right)P_o$

8. $P_u = \dfrac{a}{cs}$

Quiz

True-False

T   F   1. Like decision analysis and Markov analysis, queuing analysis is a deterministic technique.

T   F   2. The operating characteristics of a queuing system are only "average" results reached only when the system is in steady-state.

T   F   3. The major requirement for using the single server model of this chapter is a finite calling population.

T   F   4. All of the queuing formulas of this chapter require that a and s be given for the same time period.

T   F   5. The multiple server model assumes that there is a single queue feeding all of the servers.

T   F   6. The queuing formulas in this chapter cannot be used when the arrival rate does not follow the Poisson distribution.

Short Answer

7. How would you apply queuing analysis to a facility like a bank, where the arrival rate changes frequently during the day?

8. Compare the different queuing systems used at local fast-food and pizza restaurants. Which are single server and which are multiple server systems?

9. Describe why steady-state operating characteristics in queuing analysis don't always accurately represent the behavior of waiting lines.

10. Suppose two queuing systems have the same utilization factor of .70, while one system has $c = 1$ and the other system has $c = 2$. Which system should give better customer waiting times?

Problems

1. The local quick printing shop is operated by a single person. On average, 18 customers arrive each hour for photocopies. The average time per job on the copy machine is 2.5 minutes. It has been determined that customer arrivals to the shop follow the Poisson distribution while service times are exponentially distributed. Determine the following:
   a. The probability that the server is idle.
   b. The average utilization of the photocopy machine.
   c. The average number of customers in the queuing system.
   d. The average time a customer waits *before* being served.
   e. The average time a customer is in the queuing system.
   f. The probability of having no more than two customers in the queuing system.

Solution

First, it is necessary to define the queuing system as the shop, its waiting room, and the counter. We'll presume service is first-come, first-served; the customers may "take-a-number" as they come in the door.

From the problem information we can set the arrival rate $a = 18$ customers per hour. Since the average service time is 2.5 minutes per job, the *hourly* service rate is 60/2.5, or $s = 24$ jobs/hour. Note that a and s must be given for the *same* time period, in this case customers per hour.

The probability that the server is idle:

$$I = 1 - \frac{a}{s} = 1 - \frac{18}{24} = 1 - .75 = .25$$

The average utilization of the copy machine:

$$P_u = \frac{a}{s} = \frac{18}{24} = .75$$

The average number of customers in the queuing system:

$$L = \frac{a}{s-a} = \frac{18}{24-18} = 3.0 \text{ customers}$$

The average time a customer waits before being served:

$$W_q = \frac{a}{s(s-a)} = \frac{18}{24(24-18)} = .125 \text{ hours}$$
$$= .125 \text{ hours} \times 60 \text{ min/hr} = 7.5 \text{ minutes.}$$

The average time a customer is in the queuing system:

$$W = \frac{1}{s-a} = \frac{1}{24-18} = .167 \text{ hours}$$
$$= .167 \text{ hours} \times 60 \text{ min/hr} = 10 \text{ minutes}$$

or,

$$W = \frac{L}{a} = \frac{3.0}{18} = .167 \text{ hours} = 10 \text{ minutes}$$

The probability of having no more than 2 customers in the system is the sum of the probabilities of having 0, 1, or 2 customers in the system:

$$P(n \leq 2) = P_0 + P_1 + P_2$$

$$= \left(\frac{a}{s}\right)^0 \left(1 - \frac{a}{s}\right) + \left(\frac{a}{s}\right)^1 \left(1 - \frac{a}{s}\right) + \left(\frac{a}{s}\right)^2 \left(1 - \frac{a}{s}\right)$$

$$= \left[\left(\frac{a}{s}\right)^0 + \left(\frac{a}{s}\right)^1 + \left(\frac{a}{s}\right)^2\right]\left(1 - \frac{a}{s}\right)$$

$$= \left[\left(\frac{18}{24}\right)^0 + \left(\frac{18}{24}\right)^1 + \left(\frac{18}{24}\right)^2\right]\left(1 - \frac{18}{24}\right)$$

$$= (1 + .75 + .563)(.25)$$
$$= .578$$

By inference, the probability of having *more* than 2 customers in the system:

$$P(n > 2) = 1 - P(n \leq 2)$$
$$= 1 - .578$$
$$= .422$$

2. The university computer center is considering the purchase of a second high-speed printer. Each printer is capable of printing 75 average jobs per hour. An average of 60 computer jobs arrive at the printer queue each hour to be printed. Compare the following operating characteristics for one- and two-printer configurations:
   a. Probability that a job will have to wait before being printed.
   b. The average number of jobs in the system.
   c. The average time a job waits to be printed.

Solution

For both printer configurations, $a = 60$ jobs/hour and $s = 75$ jobs/hour. We'll assume that there is a single print queue serving both printers. For the two-printer configuration, $c = 2$. For the one-printer configuration ($c = 1$), we can use either the single-server formulas or the multiple-server formulas with $c = 1$. We'll use the former since they are simpler to use.

One-Printer Configuration

$$P_o = 1 - \frac{a}{s}$$

$$= 1 - \frac{60}{75}$$

$$= 0.20$$

Two-Printer Configuration

$$P_o = \frac{1}{\left[\sum_{n=0}^{c-1} \frac{1}{n!}\left(\frac{a}{s}\right)^n\right] + \frac{1}{c!}\left(\frac{a}{s}\right)^c \left(\frac{cs}{cs-a}\right)}$$

$$= \frac{1}{\frac{1}{0!}\left(\frac{60}{75}\right)^0 + \frac{1}{1!}\left(\frac{60}{75}\right)^1 + \frac{1}{2!}\left(\frac{60}{75}\right)^2 \left(\frac{150}{150-60}\right)}$$

$$= 0.429$$

$$L = \frac{a}{(s-a)}$$

$$= \frac{60}{75-60}$$

$$= 4.0 \text{ jobs in the system.}$$

$$L = \frac{as\left(\frac{a}{s}\right)^c}{(c-1)!\,(cs-a)^2} \; P_o + \frac{a}{s}$$

$$= \frac{(60)(75)\left(\frac{60}{75}\right)^2}{1!(150-60)^2} \; (.429) + \frac{60}{75}$$

$$= .953 \text{ jobs in the system}$$

$$L_q = L\left(\frac{a}{s}\right)$$

$$= 4.0\left(\frac{60}{75}\right)$$

$$= 3.2 \text{ jobs waiting}$$

$$L_q = L - \frac{a}{s}$$

$$= .953 - \frac{60}{75}$$

$$= .153 \text{ jobs waiting}$$

$$P_w = \frac{a}{s}$$

$$= \frac{60}{75}$$

$$= .80$$

$$P_w = \frac{1}{c!}\left(\frac{a}{s}\right)^c \left(\frac{cs}{cs-a}\right) P_o$$

$$= \frac{1}{2!}\left(\frac{60}{75}\right)^2 \left(\frac{150}{150-60}\right)(.429)$$

$$= (.5)\,(.64)\,(1.667)\,(.429)$$

$$= .229$$

$$W_q = \frac{a}{s\,(s-a)}$$

$$= \frac{60}{75(75-60)}$$

$$= .0533 \text{ hrs.}$$

$$= 3.2 \text{ minutes/job}$$

$$W_q = \frac{L_q}{a}$$

$$= \frac{.153}{60}$$

$$= .0026 \text{ hrs.}$$

$$= .153 \text{ minutes/job}$$

Thus by adding a second printer we can reduce the probability that a job will wait for a printer from 80% to 23% and can reduce the printer queue from 3.2 jobs to .153 jobs. Likewise, we can reduce the waiting time from over 3 minutes to less than a minute.

The Jordan Company sold and serviced small to medium-sized electric appliances on a carry-in basis. Service was an important part of their business, and they actively competed with several other firms. Each firm was able to repair several brands of appliances including Jordan's brands.

Jordan's service department employed two full-time service technicians, one of whom could repair 4 units per hour and the other 6 units per hour on average. Service times followed the exponential distribution for each repair technician. Customers arrived to Jordan's service department at a rate of 8 per hour. Service records showed that this arrival rate followed the Poisson distribution.

Each technician had his own repair lab and both were capable of repairing any appliance, although at different rates. The general manager of Jordan's was trying to decide whether to move the two technicians closer together. At the time, each technician had his own waiting area and separate waiting line. The customers generally split on a 40/60 basis, 40% going to the slower technician and 60% to the faster technician, thus keeping the waiting lines in balance.

The manager knew that if he moved the two technicians together, with a single waiting line serving both, the faster technician would help the slower technician on the tough repairs, thus making both repairmen's service rates 5 units per hour.

The manager preferred the configuration that minimized the average customer's waiting time. What should he do?

15 Simulation

Key Concepts

I. *Simulation* is a widely applied means of analyzing complex physical systems that cannot be analyzed using other management science techniques.
  - A. Simulation may be appropriate when the physical system's characteristics don't match the assumptions made by other analysis techniques.
  - B. *Probabilistic* physical systems are a common simulation application since they are difficult to analyze analytically.
  - C. Simulation *models* use mathematical formulas to represent physical systems.
  - D. Many simulation models use *random numbers* to represent physical quantities or events like demand or service times.

II. The *Monte Carlo* process is used to generate random variable values by sampling from the appropriate probability distributions.
  - A. In principle, the relative frequencies of the various random events are represented by ranges of random numbers.
  - B. The probability of each random event is the same as the probability of "drawing" a random number in that event's corresponding random number range.
  - C. Using a *random number table* to generate a random number, we can determine the random number range it falls into and the corresponding random event.
  - D. *Computers* use mathematical processes to generate *pseudo-random numbers* having the following characteristics:
    1. Uniformly distributed
    2. Should not recycle frequently
    3. No patterns in the sequence
  - E. The Monte Carlo process can be used to sample from both *discrete* and *continuous* probability distributions.

III. A simulation model generally reflects the operation of a system in the form of operating statistics.
  - A. An important step in simulation is *validating* the model to assure that the results are representative of the physical system under study.
    1. Manually derived results can be compared with a few simulation trials to check the correctness of internal relationships.
    2. The model can be divided into parts and each part can be simulated (and validated) separately.
    3. Simulation results can sometimes be compared with actual real-world data when it exists.
  - B. Other considerations in a simulation include establishing *starting and ending conditions* for the model and determining how long the simulation should be run.
  - C. *Optimal solutions* can sometimes be obtained for simulation models by employing *search techniques* to find the best combination of decision variables.
  - D. Simulation provides the manager the capability of asking "what if" questions and determining the system's probable responses.

IV. Simulation has been widely applied in a number of different areas.
  - A. Business applications include queuing, production planning and inventory control, financial planning and capital budgeting, marketing, and strategic planning.
  - B. Simulation is commonly used in environmental and resource analysis to predict the performance of complex systems before they are built.
  - C. A number of specialized simulation languages have been developed to enable a manager to build a model without requiring detailed knowledge of computer programming.

Quiz

True-False

T F 1. Building and validating a simulation model is generally easier than using other management science techniques.

T F 2. Since many analytical techniques have difficulty handling probabilistic situations, many simulation applications involve such probabilistic events.

T F 3. Most numerical simulations performed by computers follow the Del Monte method of generating random numbers.

T F 4. The probability of drawing any particular random number is the same as drawing any other random number.

T F 5. No simulation analysis can be done without using a computer.

T F 6. One of the most difficult steps in the simulation analysis is validating the model.

T F 7. Simulations consisting of relatively few trials may not provide reliable steady-state results for probabilistic events.

T F 8. Simulation analysis can be used for discrete probability distributions, but not for continuous probability functions.

T F 9. Like other management science techniques, simulation generally results in an optimal solution.

T F 10. Most analysts feel that all problems should be studied via simulation.

Short Answer

11. Under what conditions would we expect simulation results to differ from theoretical results?

12. Describe how simulation could be used in finance and marketing applications.

13. Explain how simulation can be used to find the optimal solution to a complex problem.

14. Why are starting and ending conditions important in simulation? What assumptions were made in the problems in the text?

15. Why do most computers use pseudo-random numbers instead of random numbers?

Problems

1. The county library is considering a new machine to speed book checkouts. They have estimated the number of books per patron as follows:

Table 15.1 Distribution of Books per Patron

No. of Books per Patron	Probability
0	.20
1	.30
2	.15
3	.15
4	.10
5	.05
6	.05
	1.00

Simulate the checkout process for 15 patrons. Use the first *row* of the random number table in your text. What is the average number of books per patron? Compare the simulation results with the expected value. Why are they different?

Solution

We need to determine the random number ranges for each value of the number of books per patron, x. First find the cumulative probabilities, then the corresponding random number ranges.

Table 15.2 Random Number Ranges

No. of Books per Patron (x)	Probability $P(x)$	Cumulative Probability	Random Number Range
0	.20	.20	1–20
1	.30	.50	21–50
2	.15	.65	51–65
3	.15	.80	66–80
4	.10	.90	81–90
5	.05	.95	91–95
6	.05	1.00	96–99, 00

Notice that the random number range for each value of x starts at the end of the previous range and ends at the cumulative probability (times 100) for that x value.

Next we'll generate the book demands for the 15 patrons using the first row of the random number table. It makes no difference whether we use rows or columns from the table or where we start as long as we're consistent and use consecutive numbers. Although not needed here, we could use three-digit random numbers (000–999) if the cumulative probabilities had more than two significant digits (.805 instead of .80).

Table 15.3 Randomly Generated Book Demand for 15 Patrons

Patron	Random Number	No. of Books (x)
1	39	1
2	65	2
3	76	3
4	45	1
5	45	1
6	19	0
7	90	4
8	69	3
9	64	2
10	61	2
11	20	0
12	26	1
13	36	1
14	31	1
15	62	2
		$\Sigma = 24$

The average number of books per patron is $24/15 = 1.6$. We could compare this with the analytical expected value, $E(x)$.

$$E(x) = (.20)(0) + (.30)(1) + (.15)(2) + (.15)(3) + (.10)(4) + (.05)(5) + (.05)(6) = 2.0 \text{ books}$$
per person

What would the average number of books be for the *next* 15 patrons, continuing to use the first and second rows of the random number table? (The next 15 patrons demand a total of 49 books, for an average of 3.3 books per patron.)

The difference between the three averages (1.6, 2.0, 3.3) is due to sampling variations in the random number table. The average for all 30 customers is $(24 + 49)/30 = 2.4$, which is closer to the expected value of 2.0. In fact, we would expect the steady-state average to approach 2.0 as the number of patrons simulated increases.

2. The secretary of the management department performs typing and other short services for the staff. Table 15.4 shows the time between jobs and service time characteristics for the jobs.

Table 15.4 Job Characteristic Distributions

Time Between Jobs (Minutes)	Probability	Job Time	Probability
5	.10	4	.15
10	.15	8	.30
15	.35	12	.25
20	.20	16	.20
25	.15	20	.10
30	.05		1.00
	1.00		

Simulate the secretary's morning work for four hours and calculate the following:
a. Average turnaround time per job
b. Average number of jobs waiting to be done
c. Idle time for the secretary

Assume there are no jobs waiting in the morning and use the sixth column in the random number table in your book.

Solution

Tables 15.5 and 15.6 show the random number ranges for job arrival intervals and service times.

Table 15.5 Distribution of Arrival Intervals

Arrival Interval x (minutes)	Probability $P(x)$	Cumulative Probability	Random Number Range r_1
5	.10	.10	1–10
10	.15	.25	11–25
15	.35	.60	26–60
20	.20	.80	61–80
25	.15	.95	81–95
30	.05	1.00	96–99, 00

Table 15.6 Distribution of Service Times

Service Time y (minutes)	Probability $P(y)$	Cumulative Probability	Random Number Range r_2
4	.15	.15	1–15
8	.30	.45	16–45
12	.25	.70	46–70
16	.20	.90	71–90
20	.10	1.00	91–99, 00

Table 15.7 demonstrates the simulation of several secretarial jobs arriving at the department office. We will continue to simulate jobs until the secretary has finished the job she's working on after four hours (240 minutes) have elapsed, or when 240 minutes have elapsed if she has no work to do (ending condition). We assume there are no jobs already waiting for her to do in the morning when she arrives (starting conditions).

Table 15.7 Simulation of the Management Department Secretary

Job	r_1	Arrival Interval x	Arrival Clock	Enter Service Clock	Waiting Time	Length of Queue at Entry	r_2	Service Time y	Departure Clock	Time in System
1	19	10	10	10	0	0	65	12	22	12
2	51	15	25	25	0	0	17	8	33	8
3	63	20	45	45	0	0	85	16	61	16
4	37	15	60	61	1	1	89	16	77	17
5	76	20	80	80	0	0	71	16	96	16
6	34	15	95	96	1	1	11	4	100	5
7	27	15	110	110	0	0	10	4	114	4
8	59	15	125	125	0	0	87	16	141	16
9	08	5	130	141	11	1	08	4	145	15
10	89	25	155	155	0	0	42	8	163	8
11	79	20	175	175	0	0	79	16	191	16
12	97	30	205	205	0	0	26	8	213	8
13	06	5	210	213	3	1	87	16	229	19
14	39	15	225	229	4	1	28	8	237	12
15	97	30	255	. . . to be done after lunch						
					$\overline{20}$	$\overline{5}$		$\overline{152}$		$\overline{172}$

We can see from table 15.7 that the departmental secretary processed 14 jobs during the morning shift, which lasted 240 minutes. We can calculate several operating statistics from the simulation.

$$\text{Average turnaround time} = \frac{172}{14} = 12.3 \text{ minutes/job}$$

$$\text{Average waiting time} = \frac{20}{14} = 1.4 \text{ minutes/job}$$

$$\text{Average number of jobs waiting} = \frac{5}{14} = .36 \text{ jobs}$$

$$\text{Secretary's idle time} = 240 - 152 = 88 \text{ minutes or } 37\% \text{ idle}$$

It would appear that she could handle additional work, since the average job backlog and job waiting times are low and her idle time is 37%.

From table 15.4, the expected arrival interval is 16.5 minutes, meaning that the arrival rate is 3.64 jobs/hour. The expected service time is 11.2 minutes, meaning that the service rate is 5.36 jobs/hour. Using these two average rates, we can calculate utilization for the secretary to be 68%, with 32% idle time, not far from the simulation results.

Case Johnson Industries

Johnson Industries had two loading docks where incoming raw materials were unloaded and finished products were loaded onto semitrailer trucks. The incoming shipments took much longer to unload since the cartons were usually stacked on the floor of the trailer and had to be moved by hand, while outgoing shipments usually were loaded by the pallet-load using a lift-truck. Exhibit 15.1 shows the unloading and loading times for incoming and outgoing shipments.

Exhibit 15.1 Unloading and Loading Times

Incoming Shipments		Outgoing Shipments	
Unloading Time (minutes)	Probability	Loading Time (minutes)	Probability
15	.15	15	.60
30	.25	30	.30
45	.30	45	.10
60	.20		1.00
90	.10		
	1.00		

Sam Laughner, shipping and dock superintendent, had been trying to decide whether to dedicate one of the docks for incoming shipments, and the other for outgoing loads, or to use both docks for both kinds of shipments. Loading and unloading times would remain the same for either dock. Unfortunately, finished product storage space at Johnson was severely limited, so prompt loading of outbound shipments was virtually required. Likewise, recent expansion of the Johnson plant into the truck parking area had left little maneuvering room for the waiting trucks.

Trucks arrived throughout the day at a steady pace, following the patterns shown in exhibit 15.2. Because of the bottleneck at the truck docks, workers generally worked straight through the lunch hour and rotated lunch breaks among themselves. Sam's rule for the end of the day was to load or unload any truck arriving *before* 4:00; otherwise, the truck would have to return the next day. However, there were usually no trucks waiting at 8:00 when Johnson opened.

Exhibit 15.2 Arrival Intervals

Incoming Shipments		Outgoing Shipments	
Arrival Interval (minutes)	Probability	Arrival Interval (minutes)	Probability
15	.10	10	.10
30	.20	20	.20
45	.25	30	.40
60	.25	40	.20
75	.10	50	.10
90	.10		1.00
	1.00		

Sam wanted to simulate the two dock configurations for one week, or five working days. What kind of simulation form would Sam find useful? What operating statistics should he collect? Does Johnson Industries have enough capacity with just two docks? What configuration should he use?

Simulation

16 Forecasting

Key Concepts

I. The particular forecasting method used depends on a number of factors.
   A. The *time-frame* of the forecast.
      1. Short-term (daily to 2 months)
      2. Medium-term (1 month to 1 year)
      3. Long-term (more than 1 year)
   B. Existence of *patterns* in the forecast.
      1. *Trend* (long-term movement)
      2. *Cycle* (movement up or down during a trend)
      3. *Seasonal* (periodical, repetitive movement)
   C. *Number of variables* related to the forecast.
      1. Related to time only (time-series)
      2. Dependent on other factors (regression)

II. *Time-series* methods relate the forecast to *time* using historical data. They're best suited for short-term forecasting.
   A. *Moving average* techniques smooth out fluctuations in the demand (D_t) but don't perform well with cycles or seasonality.
      1. *Simple* (N-period) moving average forecast for period t (F_t).

$$F_t = \frac{D_{t-1} + D_{t-2} + \ldots + D_{t-N}}{N}$$

      2. *Weighted* (N-period) moving average forecast.

$$F_t = \frac{w_1 D_{t-1} + w_2 D_{t-2} + \ldots + w_N D_{t-N}}{w_1 + w_2 + \ldots + w_N}$$

   B. *Exponential smoothing* is a specialized moving average method that weights the most recent past data more strongly than older past data.
      1. *Simple* exponential smoothing forecast for period $t+1$, (F_{t+1}).

$$F_{t+1} = \alpha D_t + (1 - \alpha)F_t$$

      2. *Adjusted* exponential smoothing forecast to include a smoothed trend factor, T.

$$\text{Adjusted } F_{t+1} = F_{t+1} + \left(\frac{1 - \beta}{\beta}\right)T_{t+1}$$
$$T_{t+1} = \beta(F_{t+1} - F_t) + (1 - \beta)T_t$$

      3. Both α(alpha) and β(beta) take on values between 0 and 1, usually between .01 and .3.
      4. Both exponential smoothing methods require estimates for F_0 and T_0 to start forecasting.
   C. The reliability of forecasts can be measured by the mean absolute deviation (MAD).
      1. $\text{MAD} = \dfrac{\Sigma \,|\, \text{actual} - \text{forecast} \,|}{\text{number of periods}}$
      2. Lower values for MAD indicate better forecasts.

III. *Regression* methods relate forecasts to underlying *causal* factors and are frequently used for medium-range forecasting.
   A. *Linear* regression relates one dependent variable (*y*, the forecast variable) to one independent variable (*x*, the causal variable). The basic model is $y = a + bx$.
      1. *b* is the *slope*.

$$b = \frac{\Sigma xy - n\bar{x}\bar{y}}{\Sigma x^2 - n\bar{x}^2}$$

      2. *a* is the *intercept*.

$$a = \bar{y} - b\bar{x}$$

      3. The *coefficient of determination* (r^2) indicates the strength of the explanatory power of *x* to forecast *y*.

$$r^2 = \left[\frac{n\Sigma xy - \Sigma x \Sigma y}{\sqrt{[n\Sigma x^2 - (\Sigma x)^2][n\Sigma y^2 - (\Sigma y)^2]}} \right]^2$$

      4. A value of 1.00 for r^2 means that *x* explains 100% of the variation in *y*, while a value of 0 implies that there is no relationship between *x* and *y*.
   B. *Multiple* regression relates the forecast to more than one independent variable.
      1. The basic model is $y = a + b_1 x_1 + \ldots + b_n x_n$.
      2. The more complex computations for r^2, *a*, and b_i are usually done on the computer.
   C. A *scatter diagram* can be used to graphically illustrate the relationship between two variables.
IV. Long-term forecasts are more difficult to make and analytical methods are generally not available.
   A. The factors involved are qualitative and quite complex to predict.
      1. Technology
      2. Economic conditions
      3. Political/social conditions
   B. Long-range forecasting models rely on expert opinion, judgment, surveys, and research results but their reliability is limited.

Quiz

True-False

T F   1. Time-series methods are best suited for short-range forecasts.

T F   2. The real purpose for calculating a moving average is to smooth out random fluctuations in the data.

T F   3. A simple three-period moving average forecast for period 23 would be the sum of the actual values for periods 22, 23, and 24, divided by 3.

T F   4. Most weighted moving average forecasts weight the most distant data more heavily than the most recent data.

T F   5. Exponential smoothing is a special kind of weighted moving average technique.

T F   6. Time-series forecasting methods tend to not work well with cycles or seasonal data without special adjustments.

T F   7. The coefficient of determination gives a good indication of how well an exponential smoothing model forecasts.

T F   8. In general, lower values for MAD indicate lower quality forecasts.

T F   9. Most exponential smoothing models utilize values for α (alpha) between 0 and 1, but for most cases α will be greater than .5.

T F   10. Multiple regression models relate the forecast to one or more causal (independent) variables using a mathematical model.

T F   11. Long-term forecasts are more difficult and usually less accurate than short- or medium-range forecasts.

T   F   12. It is impossible to "exactly" forecast the future, so the manager should always expect some forecast error.

Short Answer

13. Explain the difference between time-series and causal forecasting methods. Under what circumstances might it be advantageous to combine these two approaches?

14. Describe how you might choose between several values of α for the simple exponential smoothing model.

15. Why is long-range forecasting so difficult and yet so important for the organization?

16. What is the relationship between r^2, MAD, and forecast error?

Problems

1. The dormitory foods manager is trying to predict the number of weekly meals to plan. The following table shows weekly demand for the last 7 weeks.

Week	Demand Per Week
1	170
2	205
3	215
4	210
5	200
6	195
7	210

   a. Compute a three-period moving average forecast for periods 5 through 7.
   b. Using weights of 3 for the most recent week, 2 for the next most recent period, and 1 for the most distant period in the moving average, repeat part a.
   c. Which forecast appears to be the most accurate?

Solution

   a. The moving average forecast for period 5 would be the average demand for periods 2, 3, and 4. In general, the forecast for a given week would be the most recent moving average; note that the three-week moving average is centered in the second week but would be the forecast for the fourth week.

   $$\text{Forecast for Week 5} = \frac{205 + 215 + 210}{3} = \frac{630}{3} = 210.0$$

   $$\text{Forecast for Week 6} = \frac{215 + 210 + 200}{3} = \frac{625}{3} = 208.3$$

   $$\text{Forecast for Week 7} = \frac{210 + 200 + 195}{3} = \frac{605}{3} = 201.7$$

   b. The sum of the weights is $3 + 2 + 1 = 6$. The weighted moving average forecasts are calculated as in part a, except each demand is multiplied by the appropriate weight, and the sum is divided by 6.

   $$\text{Forecast for Week 5} = \frac{3(205) + 2(215) + 1(210)}{6} = \frac{1255}{6} = 209.2$$

   $$\text{Forecast for Week 6} = \frac{3(215) + 2(210) + 1(200)}{6} = \frac{1265}{6} = 210.8$$

   $$\text{Forecast for Week 7} = \frac{3(210) + 2(200) + 1(195)}{6} = \frac{1225}{6} = 204.2$$

c. We can calculate MAD values for both sets of forecasts.

$$\text{MAD (Weighted Moving Average)} = \frac{|\,200-209.2\,| + |\,195-210.8\,| + |\,210-204.2\,|}{3}$$

$$= \frac{9.2 + 15.8 + 5.8}{3} = 10.3$$

$$\text{MAD (Moving Average)} = \frac{|\,200-210.0\,| + |\,195-208.3\,| + |\,210-201.7\,|}{3}$$

$$= \frac{10 + 13.3 + 8.3}{3} = 10.5$$

Using MAD as the criterion, we would lean slightly toward the weighted moving average technique. Since the MAD values are so close, we might use other criteria such as largest absolute error (15.8 versus 13.3), or smaller average forecast error (-5.0 for moving average, -6.4 for weighted moving average).

2. Using the same weekly demand data, calculate simple and adjusted exponential smoothing forecasts for periods 5 through 7. Assume F_1 to be the average of the first three weeks and let T_1 be 0. Let α and β be .1 and .2 respectively.

Solution

a. We'll first use the simple exponential smoothing formula, $F_{t+1} = \alpha\,D_t + (1 - \alpha)F_t$. We'll assume F_1 is the average of the first three weeks, 196.7.

$$F_2 = .1D_1 + (1 - .1)F_1 = .1(170) + .9(196.7) = 194.0$$
$$F_3 = .1D_2 + .9F_2 = .1(205) + .9(194.0) = 195.1$$
$$F_4 = .1D_3 + .9F_3 = .1(215) + .9(195.1) = 197.1$$
$$F_5 = .1D_4 + .9F_4 = .1(210) + .9(197.1) = 198.4$$
$$F_6 = .1D_5 + .9F_5 = .1(200) + .9(198.4) = 198.6$$
$$F_7 = .1D_6 + .9F_6 = .1(195) + .9(198.6) = 198.2$$

b. To apply the adjusted exponential smoothing model, we need three formulas. First calculate the unadjusted forecast, $F_{t+1} = \alpha\,D_t + (1 - \alpha)F_t$. Then find the new trend value, $T_{t+1} = \beta(F_{t+1} - F_t) + (1 - \beta)T_t$. Finally calculate the adjusted forecast, Adj. $F_{t+1} = F_{t+1} + \left(\frac{1 - \beta}{\beta}\right)T_{t+1}$.

$$F_2 = .1D_1 + .9F_1 = .1(170) + .9(196.7) = 194.0$$
$$T_2 = .2(F_2 - F_1) + (1 - .2)T_1 = .2(194.0 - 196.7) + .8(0) = -.54$$
Adj. $F_2 = F_2 + \left(\dfrac{1 - .2}{.2}\right) T_2 = 194.0 + 4(-.54) = 191.8$

$$F_3 = .1D_2 + .9F_2 = .1(205) + .9(194.0) = 195.1$$
$$T_3 = .2(F_3 - F_2) + .8T_2 = .2(195.1 - 194.0) + .8(-.54) = -.21$$
Adj. $F_3 = F_3 + 4T_3 = 195.1 + 4(-.21) = 194.3$

$$F_4 = 197.1 \text{ (from part a)}$$
$$T_4 = .2(F_4 - F_3) + .8T_3 = .2(197.1 - 195.1) + .8(-.21) = .23$$
Adj. $F_4 = F_4 + 4T_4 = 197.1 + 4(.23) = 198.0$

$$F_5 = 198.4 \text{ (from part a)}$$
$$T_5 = .2(F_5 - F_4) + .8T_4 = .2(198.4 - 197.1) + .8(.23) = .44$$
Adj. $F_5 = F_5 + 4T_5 = 198.4 + 4(.44) = 200.2$

$$F_6 = 198.5 \text{ (from part a)}$$
$$T_6 = .2(F_6 - F_5) + .8T_5 = .2(198.5 - 198.4) + .8(.44) = .37$$
Adj. $F_6 = F_6 + 4T_6 = 198.5 + 4(.37) = 200.0$

$$F_7 = 198.2 \text{ (from part a)}$$
$$T_7 = .2(F_7 - F_6) + .8T_6 = .2(198.2 - 198.5) + .8(.37) = .24$$
Adj. $F_7 = F_7 + 4T_7 = 198.2 + 4(.24) = 199.2$

Case   *Davis Wood Stoves*

The Davis Company is forecasting the quarterly sales for wood stoves so that it can make hiring and ordering decisions. Bill Davis, president of the company, feels that there is a relationship between sales and advertising expenditures, but also feels sales are increasing over time. He has gathered the following data from the previous ten quarters.

Quarter	Advertising	Sales (1000s)
1	5	30
2	5	28
3	6	32
4	6	36
5	6	37
6	7	40
7	7	42
8	8	43
9	8	47
10	10	50

After talking to a marketing instructor at the local college, Bill wants to try a regression approach and compare it with an exponential smoothing time-series analysis of sales. However, he's not sure what value of α to use. Bill also thinks advertising lags behind sales by one quarter, but is uncertain how to evaluate that relationship.

Can you help Bill with his forecasting problems? Be sure to recommend a sales figure for quarter number 11.

17 Inventory Analysis with Certain Demand

Key Concepts

I. The *classical EOQ* model gives the replenishment order quantity (Q^*) that minimizes *total inventory cost*.
  - A. Assumptions
    1. Demand is known and constant.
    2. No shortages are allowed.
    3. Lead time is zero.
    4. Inventory is *instantaneously* replenished by the new order.
  - B. Total annual inventory cost (*TIC*)
    1. *Carrying cost* (C_c) is the cost to hold one unit in inventory for one year.
    2. *Ordering cost* (C_o) is the cost to place and receive one replenishment order quantity.
    3. $TIC = C_c \dfrac{Q}{2} + C_o \dfrac{D}{Q}$

  - C. The *EOQ* (Q^*) occurs where total annual carrying cost = total annual ordering cost, or at the lowest point on the *TIC* vs. Q curve.
    1. $Q^* = \sqrt{\dfrac{2C_oD}{C_c}}$

    2. The number of orders per year is annual demand (D) divided by Q^*.
  - D. The *EOQ* model with *reorder point* (R) allows for nonzero replenishment *lead time* (L), but otherwise assumes constant demand and instantaneous replenishment of inventory.
    1. $Q^* = \sqrt{\dfrac{2C_oD}{C_c}}$

    2. $R = \dfrac{LD}{365}$

    3. *Whenever the inventory level falls to R, an order for Q* should be placed; after L days that order will replenish the inventory to a level of Q* units.*

II. Other *EOQ* models relax various assumptions of the classical *EOQ* model.
  - A. Noninstantaneous receipt (*production lot size*) model.
    1. Assumptions
      a. Demand is known and constant.
      b. No shortages are allowed.
      c. Inventory is *gradually* replenished by the new order.
      d. The daily replenishment rate (r) exceeds the daily demand rate (d).
    2. $TIC = C_c \dfrac{Q}{2}\left(1 - \dfrac{d}{r}\right) + C_o \dfrac{D}{Q}$

    3. The maximum inventory level is $Q - \dfrac{Q}{r}\,d$.

    4. $Q^* = \dfrac{2C_oD}{\sqrt{C_c\left(1 - \dfrac{d}{r}\right)}}$

    5. The length of a production run is Q/r (*days*).

B. *EOQ* model with *shortages and backorders*
  1. Assumptions
     a. Demand is known and constant.
     b. Shortages and backorders are allowed to avoid keeping excessive inventory on hand.
     c. Replenishment is instantaneous.
  2. *Shortage cost* (C_s) is the cost of stocking out of one unit.
  3. $TIC = C_s \dfrac{S^2}{2Q} + C_c \dfrac{(Q - S)^2}{2Q} + C_o \dfrac{D}{Q}$
  4. $Q^* = \sqrt{\dfrac{2C_o D}{C_c}\left(\dfrac{C_s + C_c}{C_s}\right)}$
  5. *S* is the *maximum shortage level.*

     $S = Q^*\left[\dfrac{C_c}{C_c + C_s}\right]$

  6. The variables t_1 and t_2 are the times (in years) that inventory and stockouts exist, respectively, during *one order cycle.*

     $t_1 = \dfrac{Q - S}{D}$ $\qquad\qquad$ $t_2 = \dfrac{S}{D}$

  7. To find the total time that inventory and stockout conditions exist during one year, multiply t_1 and t_2 by D/Q^*, the number of orders per year.
C. The *noninstantaneous receipt model with shortages* allows both gradual replenishment and shortages.
D. The *quantity discount* model maintains all the original classical *EOQ* assumptions but allows the unit price (*P*) to be discounted if a large quantity is purchased at one time.
  1. The carrying cost percentage (P_c) must be defined as the *percentage* of the unit price to hold one unit for a year.

     $P_c = \dfrac{C_c}{P}$

  2. The *TIC* includes a new term, *PD*, representing the annual purchase cost for all units.

     $TIC = C_o \dfrac{D}{Q} + P_c \dfrac{PQ}{2} + PD$

  3. Steps to find *Q*:
     a. Calculate Q^*.

     $Q^* = \sqrt{\dfrac{2C_o D}{P_c P}}$

     b. Calculate the *TIC* for ordering Q^*, using the *appropriate* unit price for Q^* (usually the higher price).
     c. Calculate the *TIC* for the lowest quantity (*Q*) corresponding to the *discounted* price.
     d. Choose the quantity (Q^* or *Q*) with smaller *TIC*.
     e. Steps c and d should be repeated if there are additional discounted prices.

Quiz

True-False

T F 1. To be truly realistic, the assumption that demand is known with certainty must be dropped.

T F 2. The carrying cost includes the costs of placing an order for more inventory.

T F 3. The lowest point on the *TIC* vs. *Q* curve occurs where total annual carrying cost just equals total annual ordering cost.

T F 4. If lead time is 10 days, annual demand is 5,000 units, and the *EOQ* is 500 units, there will be a total of 10 orders placed in one year.

T F 5. The reorder point is the inventory level immediately after it is replenished.

T F 6. The production lot size model is appropriate to use when inventory is not instantaneously replenished.

T F 7. The maximum inventory level for the classical *EOQ* model is $Q/2$.

T F 8. Each of the *EOQ* models in this chapter provide a Q^* that minimizes the appropriate total annual carrying cost.

T F 9. The quantity discount model compares the total annual cost of the *EOQ* lot size with the total annual cost of the larger quantity needed to obtain the price discount.

T F 10. If C_c is \$1.50 and P is \$7.50, then $P_c = 5$.

T F 11. The shortage cost *EOQ* model allows shortages and backorder in order to reduce excessive inventory carrying costs.

T F 12. The daily demand rate cannot exceed the daily replenishment rate in order to use the noninstantaneous receipt model.

T F 13. The time between receiving two orders is equal to the lead time.

T F 14. If annual demand were to double, then the resulting *EOQ* should also double.

T F 15. The *EOQ* model should never be used to develop an inventory policy when demand is not constant.

Short Answer

16. Characterize the following costs as components of carrying cost, ordering cost, or neither:
    a. inventory tax and insurance
    b. unloading costs
    c. product obsolescence and inventory spoilage
    d. interest charges on inventory investment
    e. order processing, paperwork, and record keeping costs
    f. purchase agent's salary
    g. heat, light and warehouse security
    h. cost of lost sales

17. Why is the noninstantaneous receipt model sometimes called the production lot size model?

18. Give three examples of instances in which an item you tried to purchase was out of stock. Was your sale lost, or did the store backorder the item and promise it for you at some time in the future?

19. Define the terms C_s, S, t_1, t_2 as they relate to the *EOQ* model with shortages.

Problems

1. The local foundry uses 3,000 tons of scrap metal per year. The annual carrying cost is \$50 per ton while the ordering cost is \$200.
    a. Find the *EOQ* to the nearest ton.
    b. What is the *TIC*?
    c. Assuming that the lead time is 5 days, calculate the reorder point.
    d. How many orders per year will be placed?
    e. Suppose that the unit cost would drop from \$150 per ton to \$145 per ton if the company orders a minimum of 500 tons at a time. Should they do it?

Solution

First identify the relevant costs:

$$D = 3,000 \text{ tons/year}$$
$$C_c = \$50/\text{ton/year}$$
$$C_o = \$200/\text{order}$$

a. $Q^* = \sqrt{\dfrac{2C_oD}{C_c}} = \sqrt{\dfrac{2(200)(3,000)}{50}} = \sqrt{24,000} = 155 \text{ tons}$

b. $TIC = C_c\dfrac{Q}{2} + C_o\dfrac{D}{Q} = (50)\dfrac{155}{2} + (200)\dfrac{3,000}{155} = 3,875 + 3,871 = \$7,746$

Notice that holding and ordering cost are not quite equal, since we rounded Q^* to the nearest ton.

c. $L = 5$, $R = L\dfrac{D}{365} = (5)\dfrac{3,000}{365} = 41.1 \text{ tons}$

d. There will be $\dfrac{3,000}{155} = 19.4$ orders per year.

e. *Option 1*   *Option 2*
   $Q = 155 \text{ tons}$ $Q = 500 \text{ tons}$
   $P = \$150/\text{ton}$ $P = \$145/\text{ton}$

For this quantity discount problem, we need to define P_c to be the *percentage* of unit cost per year.

$$P_c = \dfrac{C_c}{P} = \dfrac{\$50}{\$150} = .333$$

We need to find the TIC for $Q^* = 155$ tons and $Q = 500$ tons (the minimum order quantity to take advantage of the lower price per ton).

For $Q^* = 155$:

$$TIC = C_o\dfrac{D}{Q} + P_cP\dfrac{Q}{2} + PD$$

$$= (200)\dfrac{3,000}{155} + .333(150)\dfrac{155}{2} + 150(3,000)$$

$$= 3,871 + 3,871 + 450,000$$

$$= \$457,742$$

For $Q = 500$

$$TIC = (200)\dfrac{3,000}{500} + .333(145)\dfrac{500}{2} + 145(3,000)$$

$$= 1,200 + 12,071 + 435,000$$

$$= \$448,271$$

Since the TIC for $Q = 500$ is \$9,471 less than the TIC for $Q^* = 155$, it appears advantageous to take advantage of the quantity discount, providing there is room to store and maintain the inventory. Note that inventory turnover drops from 19.4 in part d to $\dfrac{3,000}{500} = 6.0$ if 500 tons are ordered at a time.

2. The ACME Manufacturing Company produces 36,500 units per year. The cost to set up a production run is \$450, while the maximum daily production rate is 150 units. Annual carrying cost averages \$10 per unit, while unit cost is \$35.
   a. What is the economic production lot size?
   b. Find the maximum inventory level.
   c. What is the number of production runs per year?
   d. How many days does each production run take?
   e. How many days *between* production runs?

Solution

This company manufactures units, so we need to use the noninstantaneous receipt (production lot size) model. First, the relevant data is

$D = 36,500$ units/year
$C_o = \$450$/run
$C_c = \$10$/unit/year
$P = \$35$/unit (not used)
$r = 150$ units/day

a. To calculate Q^*, first find d, the daily demand rate.

$$d = \frac{D}{365} = \frac{36,500}{365} = 100 \text{ units/day}$$

$$
\begin{aligned}
Q^* &= \sqrt{\frac{2C_o D}{C_c}\left(1 - \frac{d}{r}\right)} \\
&= \sqrt{\frac{2(450)(36,500)}{10}\left(1 - \frac{100}{150}\right)} \\
&= \sqrt{1,095,000} \\
&= 1,046 \text{ units/run}
\end{aligned}
$$

b. The maximum inventory level is

$$
\begin{aligned}
Q - \frac{Q}{r}d &= 1,046 - \frac{1,046}{150}(100) \\
&= 1,046 - 697 \\
&= 349 \text{ units.}
\end{aligned}
$$

c. The number of production runs per year is

$$\frac{D}{Q} = \frac{36,500}{1,046} = 34.9 \text{ runs.}$$

d. Each production run takes

$$\frac{Q}{r} = \frac{1,046}{150} = 7.0 \text{ days}$$

e. The number of days between runs (from the start of one run to the start of the next run) is

$$\frac{Q}{d} = \frac{1,046}{100} = 10.5 \text{ days.}$$

3. Welsh's Bookstore is trying to decide whether to allow shortages of notebooks. They have estimated shortage cost to be the lost profit on a notebook, or $0.75. Holding cost is $1.25 per notebook per year, while ordering cost is $30. Welsh's sells about 4,000 notebooks per year. What is the *EOQ* if they allow shortages? How many days per year would they be out of stock?

Solution

First, the relevant data is

$C_s = \$0.75/\text{notebook stocked out}$
$C_c = 1.25/\text{notebook/year}$
$C_o = \$30/\text{order}$
$D = 4{,}000 \text{ notebooks/year}$

a. To calculate the *EOQ*, find the value Q*.

$$Q^* = \sqrt{\frac{2C_oD}{C_c}\left(\frac{C_s + C_c}{C_s}\right)}$$

$$= \sqrt{\frac{2(30)(4{,}000)}{1.25}\left(\frac{.75 + 1.25}{.75}\right)}$$

$$= \sqrt{512{,}000}$$

$$= 716 \text{ notebooks/order}$$

b. To calculate the number of out of stock days we first need to find S, the maximum shortage level.

$$S = (Q^*)\frac{C_c}{C_c + C_s}$$

$$= (716)\frac{1.25}{1.25 + .75}$$

$$= 448 \text{ units short}$$

$$t_1 = \frac{Q - S}{D}$$

$$= \frac{716 - 448}{4{,}000}$$

$$= .067 \text{ years}$$

$$= 24.5 \text{ days in stock}$$

$$t_2 = \frac{S}{D}$$

$$= \frac{448}{4{,}000}$$

$$= .112 \text{ years}$$

$$= 40.9 \text{ days out of stock}$$

Thus, out of each $24.5 + 40.9 = 65.4$ days, Welsh's will be in stock 24.5 days and out of stock 40.9 days. On an annual basis, they would be out of stock *228 days*.

Inventory Analysis with Certain Demand

Case *Fischer Nurseries, Inc.*

Each spring E. J. Fischer had to decide how much nursery stock should be ordered from area wholesalers. He knew that if he ordered too much, he'd have to sell it at a deep discount or end up throwing it away in the fall. Consequently, he established an unusually high obsolescence factor of 15% of unit cost.

He estimated other annual inventory costs of 15% to cover interest expenses, 3% for taxes, 2% for insurance, and 5% for miscellaneous costs, including wages for the nursery workers who cared for the stock.

Ordering costs consisted of the cost of sending a driver and truck to pick up the order, paperwork and bookkeeping costs, and other assorted expenses, and averaged about $200 per order.

Mr. Fischer had been recently approached by one of his suppliers with "an offer he couldn't turn down." As it turned out, the supplier had an oversupply of inkberry, a small but attractive shrub, and had offered a significant price reduction for a quantity purchase.

Fischer normally sold 1,500 inkberry shrubs through the year, and usually paid $10 for a mature shrub. This year he could pay $9.50 per shrub if he ordered at least 500 at a time, or he could pay $9.00 each if he ordered at least 1,000 shrubs at a time.

Should Mr. Fischer take advantage of this bargain, or should he stay with ordering the *EOQ* amount at the usual price? What will his total annual inventory cost be this year?

18 Inventory Analysis with Uncertain Demand

Key Concepts

I. The *EOQ model with safety stocks* allows us to determine the reorder point (R) when *demand is uncertain* and not constant.

 A. We determine the *EOQ* (Q^*) in the same fashion as in chapter 17.

$$Q^* = \sqrt{\frac{2C_oD}{C_c}}$$

 B. When the *stockout cost* (C_s) is known, we can choose the optimal value for the safety stock by minimizing the sum of *total annual shortage cost* and *total annual carrying cost of safety stock*.

 1. Total annual shortage cost is the *expected shortage* cost per order multiplied by the number of orders per year.

 2. Expected shortage cost is found by multiplying C_s by the *expected shortages* for each reorder point under consideration.

 3. Annual carrying cost for the safety stock is found by multiplying the safety stock (S_s) by the carrying cost, C_c.

 C. The reorder point is the sum of average demand during lead time (L) plus safety stock.

$$R = \frac{LD}{365} + S_s$$

II. When C_s is not known, or when a particular *service level* is desired, the reorder point can be set using probability concepts.

 A. *Service level* is the percentage of customers served during the lead time.

 B. Assume that demand during lead time follows the *normal distribution* and that we know μ and σ.

 C. Find the Z value corresponding to the service level.

 1. Z is the number of standard deviations (σ) the reorder point is from mean demand during lead time (μ).

 2. Subtract .5 from the service level and find the closest associated Z value from the normal table in the appendix.

 D. Safety stock is equal to $Z\sigma$.

 E. The new reorder point is the sum of average demand during lead time plus safety stock.

$$R = \mu + Z\sigma$$

III. When the frequency of ordering is already determined, we can use *payoff tables* to determine the order quantity if we know the probability of each demand value.

 A. The payoff table relates the *certain profit* for each combination of the decision variable (Q) and the demand outcome (D).

 1. P is unit selling price, C is unit cost, C_c is carrying cost over the duration of the order, and C_s is the unit shortage cost.

 2. If $Q \geq D$ (no shortage),

$$\text{Profit} = DP - QC - \frac{Q}{2}C_c.$$

 3. If $Q < D$ (shortage),

$$\text{Profit} = QP = QC - \frac{Q}{2} - C_c - C_s(D - Q).$$

4. If desired, *salvage value* could be added to the profit formula for any unsold units.
   B. The *optimal Q* will have the largest *expected profit*.
      1. Multiply each profit for a given Q and D by the probability of that demand.
      2. Sum the products across demand for each Q to calculate expected profit.
   C. The expected profit is the *average* profit over *several* weeks and will not necessarily reflect the actual results *every* period.
IV. *Simulation* is another method of determining inventory policy when demand uncertainty exists, particularly when *lead time* is not constant.
   A. It is necessary to know the demand and lead time probability distributions in order to set up the corresponding random number ranges.
   B. Choosing a particular value for Q (and possibly reorder point), simulate the random demand and calculate the period's profit (or cost).
   C. After repeating the simulated demand for several periods, calculate the average profit and compare with results for other values of Q, choosing Q to minimize costs.
   D. *Computerized* simulation would be necessary if more than one component of the model is subject to uncertainty, or if a large number of observation is desired, or if the demand distribution is continuous.

Quiz

True-False

T F   1. When demand is uncertain, the classical *EOQ* formula cannot be used to determine the order quantity.

T F   2. Reorder point is sum of average demand during lead time plus the safety stock.

T F   3. A service level of 60% means that 60% of the units demanded are not available for sale.

T F   4. Total annual shortage cost measures the average cost of carrying safety stock.

T F   5. When setting the reorder point to correspond to a specified service level, we generally assume that demand during lead time follows the normal distribution.

T F   6. Having safety stock guarantees there will never be shortages.

T F   7. When the order frequency is fixed, the best ordering policy will balance shortages and excess inventory.

T F   8. Computer simulation of inventory decisions is particularly useful when demand during lead time is constant.

T F   9. The simulated cost or profit should not be expected in *each* period, but rather is an average taken over several periods.

T F   10. None of the techniques in this chapter are appropriate when both demand *and* lead time uncertainty exist.

T F   11. When the order frequency is fixed, the order decision is how much to order, not the reorder point.

Short Answer

12. Describe the meaning of Q, R, and S_s as illustrated by figure 18.2 in the text.

13. What factors affect the amount of safety stock a company should carry?

14. Under what conditions would a computer simulation of inventory decisions be appropriate?

15. How would you calculate safety stock for a given service level if demand during lead time followed the *Poisson* probability distribution?

Problems

1. An inventory system has an annual demand of 15,000 units, while ordering cost is $100 per order and annual carrying cost is $1 per unit. Shortage cost is $0.75 per unit. The demand during lead time is defined by the following probability distribution.

Demand During Lead Time	Probability
2,000	.10
4,000	.15
6,000	.50
8,000	.15
10,000	.10
	1.00

Find the optimal safety stock and reorder point.

Solution

The relevant data is

$$D = 15,000 \text{ units,}$$
$$C_o = \$100/\text{order,}$$
$$C_c = \$1/\text{unit/year, and}$$
$$C_s = \$0.75/\text{unit short.}$$

To calculate expected demand during lead time, multiply each demand value by its probability.

$$E(\text{Demand}) = .10(2,000) + .15(4,000) + .50(6,000) + .15(8,000) + .10(10,000)$$
$$= 6,000 \text{ units}$$

Next we need to find expected shortages for several different reorder points. We'll not consider any reorder point less than the expected demand of 6,000, since that would lead to excessive shortages. The expected shortage per reorder point will be the number of units short times the probability of that demand, summed over all demand values. Safety stock is the difference between the reorder point and the expected demand during lead time of 6,000 units. Table 18.1 summarizes these calculations.

Table 18.1 Computation of Total Expected Shortages per Order

Reorder Point	Safety Stock	Actual Demand During Lead Time	Resulting Shortage	Probability of Shortage	Expected Shortage per Demand	Total Shortage per Order
6,000	0	6,000	0	.50	0	
		8,000	2,000	.15	300	700
		10,000	4,000	.10	400	
8,000	2,000	8,000	0	.15	0	
		10,000	2,000	.10	200	200
10,000	4,000	10,000	0	.10	0	0

The next step is to calculate the total annual shortage cost for each safety stock value. First, calculate the EOQ and number of orders per year.

$$Q^* = \sqrt{\frac{2C_o D}{C_c}}$$

$$= \sqrt{\frac{2(100)(15,000)}{1.00}} = 1,732 \text{ units}$$

$$\text{Number of orders per year} = \frac{15,000}{1,732} = 8.66 \text{ orders}$$

$$\text{Total annual shortage cost} = C_s \frac{D}{Q} \text{ (average shortage per order)}$$

Using the average shortages per order from table 18.1, total annual shortage costs are shown in table 18.2.

Table 18.2 Total Annual Shortage Costs

Reorder Point	Safety Stock	Expected Shortages per Order	Total Annual Shortage Cost
6,000	0	700	$4,547
8,000	2,000	200	1,299
10,000	4,000	0	0

The total annual carrying cost for safety stock is $S_s C_c$, and C_c is $1.00 per unit per year. The optimal choice for safety stock will minimize the sum of total annual shortage and safety stock carrying costs, as shown in table 18.3.

Table 18.3 Total Annual Safety Stock Cost

Reorder Point	Safety Stock	Total Annual Shortage Cost	Total Annual Safety Stock Carrying Cost	Total Annual Safety Stock Cost
6,000	0	$4,547	$ 0	$4,547
8,000	2,000	1,299	2,000	3,299
10,000	4,000	0	4,000	4,000

Thus a reorder point of 8,000 and safety stock of 2,000 minimize total annual safety stock cost.

2. The local college bookstore is trying to establish a reorder point for a popular T-shirt. The demand during lead time for this item is normally distributed with a standard deviation of 100 units. Average demand per day is 60 units while lead time averages 10 days. Determine the safety stock and reorder point for the following service levels: 80%, 90%, 95%, 99%.

Solution

We must first calculate mean demand during lead time by multiplying the average daily demand by the lead time.

$$\mu = 60(10) = 600 \text{ units}$$

Next we need to find the Z values corresponding to the service levels. From the normal table in the appendix, we find the following values.

$$Z(80\%) = .842$$

$$Z(90\%) = 1.282$$

$$Z(95\%) = 1.645$$

$$Z(99\%) = 2.326$$

The reorder point is given as

$$R = \mu + Z\sigma$$

The standard deviation of demand during lead time (σ) is 100. The four reorder point and safety stock combinations are shown in table 18.5.

Table 18.5 Reorder Point and Safety Stock Values for Various Service Levels

Service Level	Z	Safety Stock ($Z\sigma$)	Reorder Point ($\mu + Z\sigma$)
80%	.842	84	684
90%	1.282	128	728
95%	1.645	165	765
99%	2.326	233	833

Case *Hamilton Distributing Company*

Hamilton sold a wide variety of paper and janitorial products to commercial customers, including motels and restaurants, schools, and offices. Due to the bulk of many of these products and limited space at the Hamilton warehouse, replenishment orders had been placed frequently. However, due to fluctuations in delivery lead time from the manufacturer, Hamilton had been experiencing stockouts with increasing frequency.

Hamilton's inventory manager, Mike Hughes, remembered studying safety stock and reorder points in school. He decided to select a typical item that was currently out of stock and collect lead time and demand statistics for the past years. He was able to reconstruct 50 replenishment orders and 100 weeks of demand, as shown in exhibit 18.1.

A check with the accounting department showed that the ordering cost for this product was $30, while the annual demand for the previous year was 1,800 cases. Annual holding costs came to $3.00 per case, while shortage costs were estimated at $5.00 per case.

Mike decided to use a tree-diagram approach to calculate the demand during lead time values and probabilities. If the lead time to Hamilton were just one week, then the demand during that week could only be 20, 40, or 60. Likewise, if the lead time were two weeks, then the demands for the two weeks could be 20+20, 20+40, 20+60, 40+20, 40+40, 40+60, 60+20, 60+40, or 60+60. Demand during a three-week lead time would be similarly calculated. Mike started to prepare exhibit 18.2 but was called away to the telephone before he had a chance to finish the diagram.

Help Mike complete the demand during lead time calculations and fill in exhibit 18.3. Using the payoff table approach, find the optimal reorder point, safety stock, and reorder quantity that minimize total annual inventory cost. What is the expected number of shortages per year for the optimal plan?

Exhibit 18.1 Lead Time and Demand Statistics

Lead Time (weeks)	Frequency	Demand per Week	Frequency
1	10	20	40
2	25	40	40
3	15	60	20
	50		100

Exhibit 18.2 Partially completed tree diagram for demand during lead time

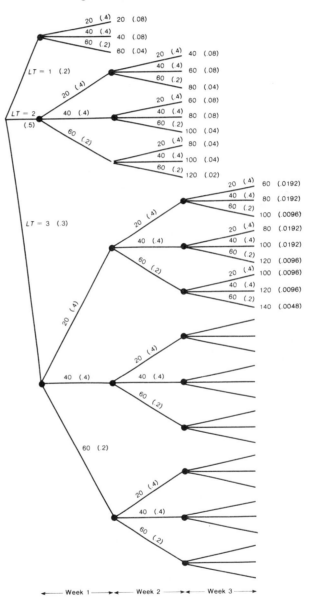

Exhibit 18.3 Demand During Lead Time Distribution

Demand During Lead Time	Probability
20	
40	
60	
80	
100	
120	
140	
160	
180	
	1.000

Inventory Analysis with Uncertain Demand

19 Network Flow Models

Key Concepts

I. A *network* is an arrangement of paths (*branches*) connecting various points (*nodes*) between which items can *flow* or move.
  A. *Nodes* are represented by circles and the number inside the circle identifies the node.
    1. The *origin* or *source* node is the beginning node in the network.
    2. The *destination* or *sink* node may be the ending node or any other node in the network, depending on the form of analysis we are using.
  B. *Branches* are represented by lines connecting two nodes. The numbers on the line may indicate distance, time, cost, or capacity along that branch.
  C. *Network flow models* have become a very popular management science tool.
    1. They are a *pictorial* means of representing complex, real-world situations, which aid a manager's comprehension of good decisions.
    2. A large number of real-life systems can be modeled as network flow models, which are relatively easy to conceive and construct.
II. The *shortest route problem* determines the shortest distance (or minimal cost) between the origin and *each* of the destination nodes in the network.
  A. The *permanent set* contains all the nodes for which we have already found the shortest path from the origin.
  B. Solution steps.
    1. Beginning with the origin, select the node with the *shortest* route from all nodes directly connected to the origin node.
    2. Add the origin node and the node from step 1 to the permanent set.
    3. Determine all nodes directly connected to the permanent set nodes.
    4. Select the node from the group in step 3 having the shortest route and add it to the permanent set.
    5. Continue steps 3 and 4 until all nodes are in the permanent set.
  C. The shortest route solution to the problem will be the paths to the nodes in the permanent set as found in steps 1 and 4.
III. The *minimal spanning tree problem* connects each node in the network with at least one other node so that the sum of the branch lengths is minimized.
  A. The *spanning tree* contains all the nodes and branches that have already been connected together.
  B. Solution steps.
    1. Beginning with the origin (or any) node, select the *closest* node directly connected to it.
    2. Add the origin node and the node from step 1 to the spanning tree.
    3. Determine all nodes not in the spanning tree but directly connected to any node in the spanning tree.
    4. Select the closest node from the group in step 3 and add it to the spanning tree.
    5. Continue steps 3 and 4 until all nodes have been added to the spanning tree.
  C. The minimal spanning tree solution to the problem will be the paths to the nodes in the final spanning tree.
  D. The main difference between this and the shortest route model lies in step 3.
    1. The shortest route approach looks at paths from the *origin* to any node not in the permanent set.
    2. The minimal spanning tree approach looks at paths from *any* node in the spanning tree to any node not in the spanning tree.
IV. The *maximal flow problem* maximizes the flow between the origin and destination nodes in the network *without exceeding* the flow capacity of any branch.
  A. Each branch has a flow *capacity* associated with flows in each direction along that branch.
    1. A *directed branch* allows only one-way flows (one of the capacities is zero).
    2. An *undirected branch* allows flow in both directions on that branch, although not necessarily with the same capacity in either direction.

B. Solution steps.
   1. Select *any* path (from origin to destination) and send the maximum flow through that path; that flow is the smallest directed capacity along the path.
   2. Calculate *net flow* along each branch of the path in step 1 and recalculate capacities.
      a. *Subtract* the flow from each directed capacity on the path.
      b. *Add* the flow to each opposite-direction capacity on the path.
   3. Pick another path arbitrarily and repeat steps 1 and 2, adding the flow to each branch along the path.
   4. Continue steps 1–3 until there are no more paths with available flow capacity.
C. The maximal flow solution to the problem will be the flows resulting from step 4. This is the maximum amount that can be sent from the origin node to the destination node.

Quiz

True-False

T F   1. We would ordinarily expect the shortest path and minimal spanning tree methods to give us the same solution.

T F   2. It is assumed that the branches in the minimal spanning tree problems have essentially unlimited capacity.

T F   3. Network flow models are applicable to a wide range of real-world problems.

T F   4. The final solution to the minimal spanning tree problem will vary, depending on the node you start with.

T F   5. A directed branch will have the same flow capacity in each direction.

T F   6. The destination node must always be the highest numbered node.

T F   7. The permanent set is associated with the maximal flow solution procedure.

T F   8. In the shortest path approach, we're concerned with the minimal distance from any node in the set to any other node not in the set.

T F   9. The net flow along a branch is the directed sum of flows in both directions on that branch.

T F 10. Once we have found the shortest path route to a node, we would not have to consider a different path to that node from the origin.

Short Answer

11. Describe the differences between the shortest route problem and the minimal spanning tree problem.

12. Why are network flow models so popular today as a management science technique?

13. What is meant by "net flow along a branch" in the maximal flow problem?

14. How would you handle *ties* for closest node in step 4 of the shortest route problem? In step 4 of the minimal spanning tree problem?

Problems

1. Find the shortest route from node 1 to each other node in the network shown in figure 19.1. The numbers on the branches are distances.

Figure 19.1

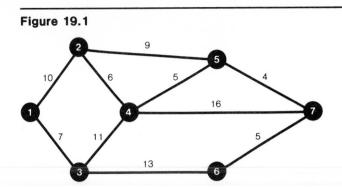

Solution

The first step is to select the shortest route from node 1 to a connected node, or branch 1–3, which is a distance of 7. Add nodes 1 and 3 to the permanent set.

Next determine the length of all paths directly connecting nodes with nodes in the permanent set. We need to consider paths 1–2, 1–3–4, and 1–3–6 having lengths 10, 7+11, and 7+13 respectively. The shortest path (1–2) is selected and node 2 is added to the permanent set.

Table 19.1 details the remaining steps in the complete solution to this shortest path problem. "Stage" refers to the sequential decisions made in steps 3 and 4. Table 19.2 shows the optimal path to each destination.

Table 19.1 The Shortest Path Solution Stages

Stage	Permanent Set	Possible Branches	Branch Distance
1	1	1–2	10
		1–3	7*
2	1,3	1–2	10*
		3–4	7+11=18
		3–6	7+13=20
3	1,2,3	2–4	10+6=16*
		2–5	10+9=19
		3–4	7+11=18
		3–6	7+13=20
4	1,2,3,4	2–5	10+9=19*
		3–6	7+13=20
		4–5	16+5=21
		4–7	16+16=32
5	1,2,3,4,5	3–6	7+13=20*
		4–7	16+16=32
		5–7	19+4=23
6	1,2,3,4,5,6	4–7	16+16=32
		5–7	19+4=23*
		6–7	20+5=25
7	1,2,3,4,5,6,7	—	—

Table 19.2 The Optimal Shortest Path Solution

From Node 1 to Node	Path to the Node	Distance
1	–	–
2	1–2	10
3	1–3	7
4	1–2–4	16
5	1–2–5	19
6	1–3–6	20
7	1–2–5–7	23
		95

2. Given the network shown in figure 19.2 with the flow capacities along each branch, determine the maximum flow from origin node 1 to destination node 6, and the flow along each branch.

Figure 19.2

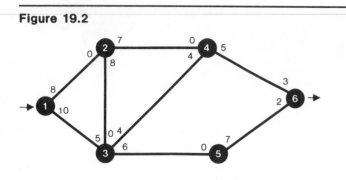

Solution

First select a path from node 1 to node 6 arbitrarily, say 1–2–4–6. The maximum flow along this path is the minimum of the flow capacities on this path (8,7,5), or 5. Calculate net flow along this path, as shown in figure 19.3.

Figure 19.3 Maximal flow for path 1–2–4–6.

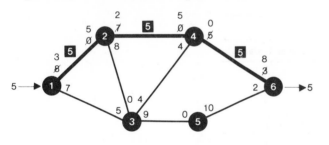

Next we choose another path arbitrarily, say 1–3–5–6. The maximum flow on this path is the minimum of (7,9,10), or 7, as shown in figure 19.4.

Figure 19.4 Maximal flow for path 1–3–5–6.

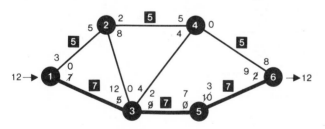

Only one path remains with available flow capacity, 1–2–3–5–6. The maximum flow on this path is the minimum of (3,8,2,3), or 2, as shown in figure 19.5. The maximal flow through the network is 14, with the flows on each branch as shown in figure 19.5. Only branch 3–4 has no flow.

Network Flow Models

Figure 19.5 Maximal flow for path 1–2–3–5–6.

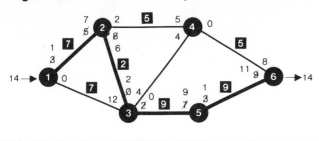

Case *National Video Cable*

In estimating its network costs prior to submitting a bid for the city cable television franchise, National Video had prepared a utility grid map of the city, shown in exhibit 19.1. The nodes in the diagram represented booster/concentrator stations while the numbers on the branches represented the running distance, in thousands of feet, between the stations using existing telephone company utility poles and right-of-way.

National Video had negotiated a contract with the telephone company to piggyback their television cable alongside the telephone service at a cost of $0.20 per running foot. Herm Newton, general manager of National Video, thought that National might have to string some of their own poles and prepared exhibit 19.2, showing the additional routes where right-of-way was available. He estimated a cost of $0.80 per foot to construct new utility poles.

He decided to compare the cost of using *only* telephone company poles with the costs of using a combination of both. What can you recommend to Herm? Should National construct any of its own poles? What is the minimum-cost spanning tree that connects all of the stations?

Exhibit 19.1 Network of rented telephone company cable paths.

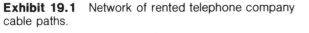

Exhibit 19.2 Network of potential cable paths that could be constructed by National.

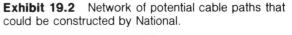

20 CPM and PERT Network Analysis

Key Concepts

I. *CPM* and *PERT* are network analysis techniques used in *planning* and *scheduling* a *project.*
  A. The *critical path method* (CPM) is used when activity durations are *deterministic* (one time for each activity).
  B. The *project evaluation and review technique* (PERT) is used when activity durations are *probabilistic* (three time estimates for each activity).
  C. *Nodes* indicate the beginning and termination points (*events*) of each activity. Nodes are traditionally numbered so that $j > i$ for activity $i \rightarrow j$.
  D. *Branches* represent activities in the project.
    1. The branch is *directed,* with the arrow pointing to the event that ends the activity and begins the next activity.
    2. The arrows indicate *precedence,* where one activity must precede another.
    3. When an activity is completed at a node, that node has been *realized.*
    4. *Concurrent* activities can be done at the same time and don't depend on one another.
    5. *Dummy* activities show precedence but don't represent any actual passage of time.
  E. The *graphical picture* of the project can provide much information to the manager, particularly in scheduling activities to assure timely completion of the project.
II. The CPM technique involves determining the *critical path,* which is the longest path through the network, or the minimum time in which the project can be finished.
  A. Solution steps.
    1. Make a *forward pass* through the network, starting at the origin node, and calculate *earliest event time* (*ET*) for each node.
      a. The *ET* is the earliest time an event could be realized.
      b. $ET_j = \text{maximum } (ET_i + t_{ij})$

      where i = starting node number for all activities ending at node j
      t_{ij} = time for activity $i \rightarrow j$

    2. Continue step 1 until the *ET* for the final node is calculated thus giving the project completion time (critical path time).
    3. Starting at the final node, make a *backward pass* through the network and determine the *latest event time* (*LT*) for each node.
      a. The *LT* is the latest time an activity can start without delaying the project beyond the critical path time.
      b. $LT_i = \text{minimum } (LT_j - t_{ij})$

      where j = ending node number of activities starting at node i
      t_{ij} = time for activity $i \rightarrow j$

    4. Continue step 3 until the *LT* for the origin node is found. If the *LT* and *ET* for the origin node aren't equal, a mistake in the forward or backward pass is likely.
    5. Calculate *activity slack* for each activity in the project.

      $\text{slack } (i \rightarrow j) = LT_j - ET_i - t_{ij}$

  B. The *critical path* consists of all activities in the network having no slack. There may be more than one critical path.
    1. No *single* activity can be delayed (beyond its *ET*) by more than its slack without delaying the project.
    2. Critical path activities cannot be delayed without delaying the project.

3. When several activities have *shared slack,* the *total* delay for the activities cannot exceed the shared slack without delaying the project.

III. The PERT technique uses three time estimates for an activity's duration but is essentially similar to CPM.
    A. The three estimates are made *subjectively.*
        1. The *optimistic* time is *a.*
        2. The *most likely* time is *m.*
        3. The *pessimistic* time is *b.*
    B. The three time estimates are used to estimate an activity's mean duration (*t*) and variance (*v*).

$$1.\ t = \frac{a + 4m + b}{6}$$

$$2.\ v = \left[\frac{b - a}{6} \right]^2$$

    C. Once t_{ij} and v_{ij} are found for each activity, the critical path is found in the same fashion as in the CPM network.
    D. PERT can be used to provide *probabilistic information* on project completion time.
        1. The project completion (critical path) time is assumed to follow the normal distribution with mean (t_p) and variance (v_p)
            a. $t_p = \Sigma$ (t_{ij} along critical path)
            b. $v_p = \Sigma$ (v_{ij} along critical path)
        2. To determine the probability that the project time will exceed some time (*x*), first calculate the *Z* value.

$$Z = \frac{x - t_p}{\sqrt{v_p}}$$

        3. The corresponding probability is found in the normal table in the appendix of your text.
    E. Although PERT has received some theoretical criticism, particularly with regard to making the time estimates, its usefulness in scheduling projects outweighs the drawbacks.

Quiz

True-False

T F   1. In CPM the activities are represented by *branches,* while with PERT the activities are represented by *nodes.*

T F   2. The arrow on a directed branch indicates *precedence,* where the activity on that branch must precede the activity immediately following that branch.

T F   3. Concurrent activities generally share the same beginning and ending nodes.

T F   4. A dummy activity may be omitted from the network since it has no duration.

T F   5. Nodes are usually numbered so that $i > j$ for activity $i{\Rightarrow}j$.

T F   6. It is impossible to have more than one critical path in a project.

T F   7. No activity $i{\Rightarrow}j$ can normally be completed before the ET_j without expediting.

T F   8. All the nodes on the critical path will have their $ET = LT$.

T F   9. If the LT for the origin node is *less than* the ET at the node, it is likely that a mistake was made on the forward or backward pass.

T F   10. If two activities have shared slack of 10, each can be delayed by 10 without delaying the project completion time.

T F   11. In a PERT analysis, the optimistic time will almost always be greater than the pessimistic time.

T F   12. Once the activity times are determined, the critical path in PERT is found the same way as in CPM.

Short Answer

13. Describe the differences between the CPM and PERT network analysis techniques.

14. What do the nodes, branches, and arrows mean in the CPM technique?

15. Is it possible for an activity to be on the critical path and have positive slack at the same time?

16. Explain how a project manager could use CPM or PERT to plan or schedule a project.

17. What is meant by the concept, shared slack?

18. Can the late time ever be *less* than the early time at a given node? What would cause that condition?

Problems

1. In the CPM network described in table 20.1 draw the network and find the *ET* and *LT* for each node. Which activities are on the critical path?

Table 20.1 CPM Network Activity Times

Activity	Time (Weeks)
1-2	10
1-3	6
2-4	2
3-4	4
3-5	6
4-6	6
5-6	3
6-7	2

Solution

First, we must draw the network, as shown in figure 20.1, including activity time. Notice activity 3–5 "bridges" over activity 2–4.

Figure 20.1 CPM network

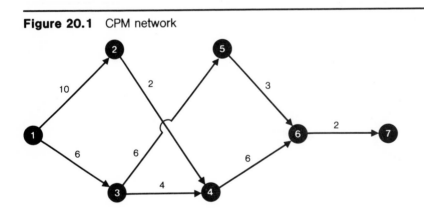

Next we'll make a forward pass from node 1 to node 7 in order to calculate ETs. By definition, $ET_1 = 0$ (node 1 is the origin node). In general,

$$ET_j = \text{maximum } (ET_i + t_{ij}).$$
$$ET_2 = ET_1 + t_{12} = 0 + 10 = 10$$
$$ET_3 = ET_1 + t_{13} = 0 + 6 = 6$$
$$ET_4 = \text{maximum } (ET_2 + t_{24}, ET_3 + t_{34})$$
$$\qquad = \text{maximum } (10 + 2, 6 + 4)$$
$$\qquad = 12$$
$$ET_5 = ET_3 + t_{35} = 6 + 6 = 12$$
$$ET_6 = \text{maximum } (ET_4 + t_{46}, ET_5 + t_{56})$$
$$\qquad = \text{maximum } (12 + 6, 12 + 3)$$
$$\qquad = 18$$
$$ET_7 = ET_6 + t_{67} = 18 + 2 = 20 \text{ weeks}$$

Thus, the project will take 20 weeks to complete. Next we'll find the LTs. By definition, the LT of the *final* node is its ET, or $LT_7 = 20$. In general,

$$LT_i = \text{minimum } (LT_j - t_{ij}).$$
$$LT_6 = LT_7 - t_{67} = 20 - 2 = 18$$
$$LT_5 = LT_6 - t_{56} = 18 - 3 = 15$$
$$LT_4 = LT_6 - t_{46} = 18 - 6 = 12$$
$$LT_3 = \text{minimum } (LT_4 - t_{34}, LT_5 - t_{35})$$
$$\qquad = \text{minimum } (12{-}4, 15{-}6)$$
$$\qquad = 8$$
$$LT_2 = LT_4 - t_{24} = 12 - 2 = 10$$
$$LT_1 = \text{minimum } (LT_2 - t_{12}, LT_3 - t_{13})$$
$$\qquad = \text{minimum } (10{-}10, 8{-}6)$$
$$\qquad = 0$$

Since for node 1, $ET = LT = 0$, our arithmetic is confirmed. Figure 20.2 shows the ET and LT values, along with the critical path.

Figure 20.2   CPM network with ET, LT and critical path

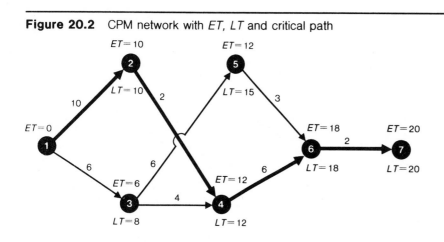

CPM and PERT Network Analysis

We can see that the critical path includes activities 1–2, 2–4, 4–6, and 6–7, all of which have no activity slack. In general,

$$\text{slack } (i\text{–}j) = LT_j - ET_i - t_{ij}$$
$$\text{slack } (1\text{–}2) = LT_2 - ET_1 - t_{12} = 10 - 0 - 10 = 0*$$
$$\text{slack } (1\text{–}3) = LT_3 - ET_1 - t_{13} = 8 - 0 - 6 = 2$$
$$\text{slack } (2\text{–}4) = LT_4 - ET_2 - t_{24} = 12 - 10 - 2 = 0*$$
$$\text{slack } (3\text{–}4) = LT_4 - ET_3 - t_{34} = 12 - 6 - 4 = 2$$
$$\text{slack } (3\text{–}5) = LT_5 - ET_3 - t_{35} = 15 - 6 - 6 = 3$$
$$\text{slack } (4\text{–}6) = LT_6 - ET_4 - t_{46} = 18 - 12 - 6 = 0*$$
$$\text{slack } (5\text{–}6) = LT_6 - ET_5 - t_{56} = 18 - 12 - 3 = 3$$
$$\text{slack } (6\text{–}7) = LT_7 - ET_6 - t_{67} = 20 - 18 - 2 = 0*$$

* (denotes critical path activity)

Notice that activities 3–5 and 3–6 have *shared slack* of 3 weeks, while activities 1–3 and 3–4 have shared slack of 2 weeks.

2. Table 20.2 shows the network activities and their PERT time estimates. Find t and v for each activity and draw the network. Which activities are on the critical path? What is the probability that the project will take at least 21 weeks?

Table 20.2 PERT Network Activity Times

Activity	Time Estimates (Weeks)		
	a	m	b
1–2	6	10	14
1–3	1	7	7
1–4	2	2	2
2–5	2	4	6
3–5	6	6	6
4–6	5	5	11
5–6	1	3	5
6–7	1	2	3

Solution

To calculate t and v,

$$t = \frac{a + 4m + b}{6}$$

$$v = \left[\frac{b - a}{6}\right]^2$$

$$t_{12} = \frac{6 + 4(10) + 14}{6} = 10$$

$$v_{12} = \left[\frac{14 - 6}{6}\right]^2 = 16/9$$

$$t_{13} = \frac{1 + 4(7) + 7}{6} = 6$$

$$v_{13} = \left[\frac{7 - 1}{6}\right]^2 = 1$$

The remaining calculations are summarized in table 20.3.

Table 20.3 PERT Time Calculations

	Time Estimates (Weeks)			Mean Time	Variance
	a	m	b	t	v
1–2	6	10	14	10	16/9
1–3	1	7	7	6	1
1–4	2	2	2	2	0
2–5	2	4	6	4	4/9
3–5	6	6	6	6	0
4–6	5	5	11	6	1
5–6	1	3	5	3	4/9
6–7	1	2	3	2	1/9

The PERT network is shown in figure 20.3, along with *ET*, *LT*, and the critical path.

Figure 20.3 PERT mean, variance, and critical path

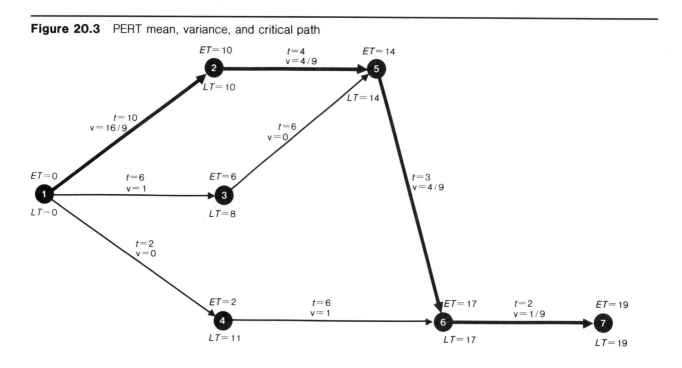

Table 20.4 shows how we calculate the project mean time (t_p) and variance (v_p).

Table 20.4 PERT Project Mean Time and Variance

Critical Path Activity	Mean Time	Variance
1–2	10	16/9
2–5	4	4/9
5–6	3	4/9
6–7	2	1/9
	$t_p = 19$ weeks	$v_p = 25/9$ = 2.78 weeks

To determine the probability that this project will take at least 21 weeks, we must first calculate the Z value.

$$Z = \frac{x - t_p}{\sqrt{v_p}}$$
$$= \frac{21 - 19}{\sqrt{2.78}}$$
$$= 1.20$$

The probability that the project will take at least 21 weeks is the same as the probability that Z is at least 1.20. From the normal table, we find that the corresponding probability is .1151. Thus, there is a 12% chance the project will take at least 21 weeks, or an 88% chance that it will take no longer than 21 weeks.

Case *Lundell Construction*

Lundell Construction was a small commercial builder specializing in renovating old buildings into modern office space. One goal of the firm was to keep the exterior charm of the old building while making the interior functional for the modern office. Due to the high risk involved with urban renewal projects, Lundell required considerable prepayment from their customers. In turn, Lundell agreed to enter into a binding delivery contract, with stiff penalties for late completion of the project.

One such renovation project is illustrated in exhibit 20.1. These 14 activities comprised the fundamental stages in a project that Lundell had promised in 40 days, with a penalty of $300 for each day over 40 that the project is unfinished. The site foreman, Jim Edwards, had applied CPM in the past and thought it might be useful on this project.

Since bad weather and material delivery problems had often delayed projects, Jim prepared a list of activities that could be expedited, shown in exhibit 20.2. Expediting usually involved renting a special machine, pulling Lundell crews off other jobs, hiring extra help, or subcontracting work to other builders in order to finish the activity more quickly.

Draw the CPM network and determine the critical path. Which activities have slack? Can Lundell make the 40 day deadline? If not, what activities should be expedited in order to minimize cost penalties?

Exhibit 20.1 Activities for Lundell Building Renovation Project

Activity	Precedent Activities*	Time (Days)
A	—	10
B	A	4
C	A	3
D	B	2
E	C,D	5
F	C	4
G	C	12
H	G	3
I	H	7
J	E	1
K	G,I	2
L	J,K	13
M	G	12
N	M,L	4

* Each precedent activity must be completed before the activity at left can begin.

Exhibit 20.2 Activity Expediting Cost

Activity	Maximum No. of Days	Cost per Day
A	2	$250
E	1	150
F	1	100
I	1	50
L	3	250
M	4	125
N	1	200

21 Dynamic Programming

Key Concepts

I. *Dynamic programming* is a solution *approach* (not a technique) through which a large problem is subdivided into smaller subproblems and solved in *stages*.
   A. The smaller subproblems (*stages*) are solved sequentially, leading to the overall optimal solution.
   B. At each *stage* there will be one or more *states,* which can indicate the status of the system or the level of remaining resources at that stage, depending on the kind of problem.
   C. Given each state, one or more *decisions* are possible, each of which results in a *return.*
   D. For each state, the best decision is determined as the one that results in the greatest return.
   E. The *transition function* relates these states and decisions to the *next* states and decisions at the *next* stage.
   F. The optimal decision at the second stage is based on the best *total return* resulting from the joint decisions at the second stage and the corresponding best decision at the previous stage.
   G. The solution proceeds through all stages until the final stage is reached. The *sequence of optimal decisions* resulting from applying the dynamic programming method to the stages should be the optimal solution for the original large problem.

II. Applications of dynamic programming include capital investment analysis, inventory control, production planning, job-shop scheduling, plant maintenance, sales planning, and energy development.
   A. In the *salesforce* example from the text, dynamic programming was used to allocate salespersons to sales regions.
      1. The *stages* were the three sales regions.
      2. The *states* were the number of salespersons available at that stage to allocate.
      3. The *decisions* were the number of salespersons to allocate to a particular region.
      4. The *returns* were the results of allocating a specific number of salespersons to a given region.
   B. In the *knapsack* example from the text, dynamic programming was used to determine how many items to pack in a knapsack.
      1. The *stages* were the three different kinds of items that could be packed in the knapsack.
      2. The *states* were the number of pounds left to be filled.
      3. The *decisions* were the number of items of the given kind to be packed.
      4. The *returns* were the profits resulting in packing (and later reselling) the given mix of items.
   C. In the *stagecoach* example from the text, dynamic programming was used to determine the minimum time trip through a network of alternative transportation routes.
      1. The *stages* were the different legs of the journey, starting with the final leg as the first stage.
      2. The *states* were the starting points possible for a given leg of the journey.
      3. The *decisions* were which route to take on that given leg.
      4. The *returns* were the route (trip) times associated with a given set of routes.

Quiz

True-False

T   F   1. A major advantage of dynamic programming is its ability to generate a sequence of small problems that are easily solved.

T   F   2. Dynamic programming is very popular due to the ease in which the model can be understood and developed.

T   F   3. One limitation of dynamic programming is that it cannot handle more than one state variable.

T F   4. Once the *best* decision for a given state is determined, we no longer need to consider any of the other decisions for that state.

T F   5. Dynamic programming can be an alternative methodology to other management science techniques developed in the text.

T F   6. The transition function is used to define how the stages in a dynamic programming model are interrelated.

Short Answer

7. Discuss the similarities between simulation and dynamic programming as solution approaches.

8. Describe the dynamic programming model for a knapsack problem in which the volume and weight capacities of the knapsack were limited. How does this two-state variable problem differ from the one in the text?

9. If we had started in a different sales region in the salesforce example (stage 1 is the northern region), would we have chosen a different solution? Explain.

Problems

1. The Hartland Foundry has three identical machine centers in which it can produce three different products (X, Y, Z). Any product can be produced in any of the machine centers, and none of the products has a minimum production requirement. The weekly expected profits are shown in table 21.1.

Table 21.1 Expected Profit per Product

Machine Centers Scheduled	Expected Profit ($/Week)		
	Product X	Product Y	Product Z
0	$-200	$-300	$-400
1	800	500	400
2	1,700	1,700	1,700
3	2,900	2,600	2,600

Using dynamic programming, determine the optimal assignment of products to the machine center.

Solution

Since the machine centers are identical, this problem reduces to determining how many machine centers to schedule for each of the products in order to maximize return.

We'll let the *stages* of our model be the three products, *arbitrarily* choosing product X for stage 1, Y for stage 2, and Z for stage 3. The *states* for each stage will be the number of unallocated machines for that and previous stages. The *decisions* for each state will be the number of machines to allocate to that product (stage). The *returns* are the expected profits shown in table 21.1.

The general steps in the solution will be to choose the best (highest profit) decision in stage 1 for each of the states. Then, define states for stage 2 and, for each state, choose the best *joint* decision for stages 2 and 1 that maximizes *total profit* for both stages. Finally, for each state of stage 3, choose the best joint decision for stages 3 and 2 that maximizes total profit for both stages. Of course, the return at stage 2 includes the profit for the optimal decision at stage 1 as well as stage 2.

Stage 1—Allocation to Product X

Table 21.2 shows the four possible states of 0, 1, 2, and 3 machines available, decisions at each state and associated returns. For each state the optimal decision is to allocate as many machines to product X as possible.

Table 21.2   Stage 1: Optimal Decisions (*) for Each State

State 1: Machines Available for X	Decision 1: Machines to Allocate to X	Return 1: Profit
0	0*	−200*
1	0	−200
	1*	800*
2	0	−200
	1	800
	2*	1,700*
3	0	−200
	1	800
	2	1,700
	3*	2,900*

Stage 2—Allocation to Product Y

The stage 2 states and decisions are essentially the same as for stage 1, but the best decision for each state is determined by looking at the *total* profit for states 2 *and* 1. Table 21.3 illustrates the states and decisions at stage 2.

Table 21.3   Stage 2: Optimal Decisions (*) for Each State

State 2: Machines Available for Y, X	Decision 2: Machines to Allocate to Y	Return 2: Profit for Y	State 1: Machines Available for X	Return for Best State 1 Decision	Total Return: $Y+X$
0	0*	−300	0*	−200	−500*
1	0*	−300	1*	800	500*
	1	500	0	−200	300
2	0	−300	2	1,700	1,400
	1	500	1	800	1,300
	2*	1,700	0*	−200	1,500*
3	0*	−300	3*	2,900	2,600*
	1	500	2	1,700	2,200
	2	1,700	1	800	2,500
	3	2,600	0	−200	2,400

Note that *all* the machines available (column 1) are allocated to Y or X (columns 2 and 4) as determined by the transition function.

From table 21.3 we can see that the optimal decision for Y (stage 2) depends partly on the decision we make for X (stage 1). If there are no machines available for Y and X, allocate none to Y and X. If there is one machine available, assign it to X. If there are two machines available, assign both to Y. If there are three machines available, assign all three to X.

Stage 3—Allocation to Product Z

The stage 3 states and decisions are found in the same manner as in stage 2 and are shown in table 21.4. However, we must assume that all three machines are available at this stage since there are no further stages (products) to consider. Notice that we don't need to carry any stage 1 data in table 21.4: we already know what to do for stage 1 for each state in stage 2 (from table 21.3).

Table 21.4   Stage 3: Optimal Decision (*) for State 3

State 3: Machines Available for Z, Y, X	Decision 3: Machines to Allocate to Z	Return 3: Profit for Z	State 2: Machines Available for Y, X	Return for Best State 2 Decision	Total Return: $Z+Y+X$
3	0*	−400	3*	2,600	2,200*
	1	400	2	1,500	1,900
	2*	1,700	1*	500	2,200*
	3	2,600	0	−500	2,100

Since we've determined the optimal decision(s) for the final state, we can determine the optimal allocation for all three products. Since there are two solutions with the same total return, we have alternative optimal solutions.

The first solution will allocate no machines to product Z, leaving three machines for stage 2. The best choice at stage 2 (given three machines to allocate to Y and X) is to assign all three to X and none to Y.

The second optimal solution allocates two machines to product Z, leaving one to allocate at stage 2 to Y and X. From table 21.3, the best choice (given one machine to allocate) is to assign it to X, and none to product Y. Both solutions produce an expected profit of $2,200 per week.

2. Figure 21.1 shows a three-leg stagecoach problem in which we are trying to get from node 1 to node 8 as quickly as possible. Use dynamic programming to determine the optimal route that minimizes total trip time.

Figure 21.1 Network of travel routes and travel times (days)

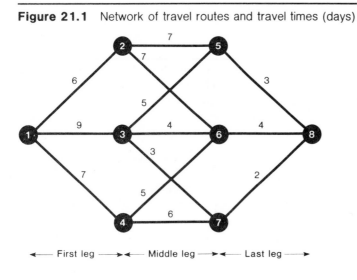

←— First leg —→←— Middle leg —→←— Last leg —→

Solution

In this problem we'll let the three legs represent *stages* in the solution. Following the example in the text, we'll let the last leg be stage 1, the middle leg will be stage 2, and stage 3 will be the first leg.

The *states* for each stage will be the starting locations for that leg of the journey. *Decisions* will be the routes taken on that leg, given the starting location. *Return* is the trip time for that (and previous) branch. In this problem we want to *minimize* total return.

Stage 1—The Last Leg

There are three beginning states in the last leg—5, 6, and 7. Table 21.5 shows the optimal decision for each state.

Table 21.5 Stage 1: Optimal Decisions (*) for Each State

State 1: Start at	Decision 1: Route to Take	Return 1: Route Time
5*	5-8*	3*
6*	6-8*	4*
7*	7-8*	2*

Since there is only one decision for each state in stage 1, that decision is optimal.

Stage 2—The Middle Leg

There are three beginning states in this leg—2, 3, and 4. Table 21.6 shows the optimal decision for each state. From node 2, it is best to follow 2-5-8. From node 3, it is best to follow 3-7-8. From node 4, it is best to follow 4-7-8.

Table 21.6 Stage 2: Optimal Decisions (*) for Each State

State 2: Start at	Decision 2: Route to Take	Return 2: Route Time	State 1: Start at	Return for Best State 1	Total Return
2	2-5*	7	5*	3	10*
	2-6	7	6	4	11
3	3-5	5	5	3	8
	3-6	4	6	4	8
	3-7*	3	7*	2	5*
4	4-6	5	6	4	9
	4-7*	6	7*	2	8*

Stage 3—The First Leg

There is only one state on the first leg; we start from node 1. Table 21.7 shows the optimal decision at this stage.

Table 21.7 Stage 3: Optimal Decision (*) for State 3

State 3: Start at	Decision 3: Route to Take	Return 3: Route Time	State 2: Start at	Return for Best State 2	Total Return
1	1-2	6	2	10	16
	1-3	9	3*	5	14*
	1-4	7	4	8	15

Since stage 3 is the final stage, we can determine the optimal solution for the complete journey. Table 21.7 shows it is best to travel from the origin node to node 3. Table 21.6 indicates that from node 3 the quickest path is to node 7, and table 21.5 shows the only path from node 7 is to node 8. Thus the fastest trip is 1–3–7–8, which takes 14 days.

Case *Griffin Electronics*

Griffin Electronics was a large national distributor of consumer electronics, including stereo, video, and personal computer systems. Charles Harris, marketing manager for Griffin, had been pondering a new product introduction plan. His advertising and promotion budget for the next six months totaled $5 million, but he wasn't sure how to best spend the funds.

He had identified at least three promotion alternatives: television commercials, magazine and newspaper ads, and a direct mail campaign. Harris' advertising agency had estimated the number of serious prospects each alternative would attract for a given expenditure, as shown in exhibit 21.1. While television had the biggest payoff, it also required the most expenditure before reaching that large audience.

Charles decided to use dynamic programming to allocate the promotion funds to the three media. He thought the three alternatives could be the stages in his model, while the state variable could be the funds available at a given stage. The decision would be to determine how much of the promotion budget to allocate to each alternative, using the objective of maximizing the number of projects generated.

How should Charles allocate the promotion budget? What is the average promotion cost per prospect?

Exhibit 21.1 Thousands of Prospects Generated per Expenditure Level

Expenditure ($ millions)	TV	Newspaper/ Magazine	Direct Mail
0	0	0	0
1	5	15	10
2	20	25	20
3	30	35	30
4	50	40	35
5	60	40	35

Key Concepts

I. The purpose of break-even analysis is to determine the number of units of a product to produce that will equate total revenue with total cost.

   A. The three components of break-even analysis are volume, cost, and profit.

      1. Volume, the level of production, also can be expressed as quantity dollar volume, or a percentage of available capacity.

      2. Costs are divided as to fixed and variable, and total cost is the sum of total fixed cost and the product of variable cost per unit and the volume, or

$$TC = c_f + v \cdot c_v$$

      3. Profit is the difference between total revenue and total cost, where total revenue is the product of volume and the price per unit, or

$$Z = v \cdot p - c_f - v \cdot c_v$$

   B. If price and costs are considered to be fixed, then we can solve for the break-even volume.

      1. Volume can be expressed as sales volume by multiplying the break-even quantity volume by the price per unit.

      2. Volume can be expressed as a percentage of total capacity by dividing the break-even quantity volume by the maximum operating capacity.

      3. The break-even point changes with changes in price or costs that can be determined by substituting the revised values into the break-even formula.

$$v = \frac{c_f}{p - c_v}$$

II. When nonlinear profit and cost relationships exist, break-even analysis requires a calculus solution, the subject of chapter 23.

Quiz

True-False

T F   1. Break-even volume tells how much should be produced to make fixed costs equal variable costs.

T F   2. Break-even volume is affected by both cost and profit.

T F   3. To express volume in terms of dollars, multiply volume by profit per unit.

T F   4. Total cost is independent of volume.

T F   5. It is impossible to evaluate the effect on break-even volume of simultaneous changes in price and cost.

Exercises

6. If $p = \$5.00$, $c_f = \$500$, and $c_v = \$.30$, find the break-even volume.

7. What is the break-even dollar volume in question 6?

8. If the capacity of the plant is 150 units, what is the volume break-even in question 6 expressed as a percentage?

9. If the price in question 6 drops to $4.00, what is the break-even volume?

10. If the fixed costs in question 6 increase by $100, what will the new break-even volume be?

Problems

1. The students of Central College are producing a yearbook. Their contract with the publisher specifies a fixed cost of $20,000 and a variable cost of $3.00 per book. If the book is priced at $12.00 per copy, how many books would need to be sold to break even?

Solution

The total cost of producing the book is

$$TC = \$20,000 + \$3 \cdot v$$

where v = volume. The total revenue is

$$TR = \$12 \cdot v$$

The total profit is the difference between total revenue and total cost, and the break-even volume is found by letting profit equal zero, or by equating revenue and cost.

$$\$12 \cdot v = \$20,000 + \$3 \cdot v$$
$$9v = 20,000$$
$$v = \frac{20,000}{9} = 2,222.2$$

So the break-even volume should be considered to be 2,223 books.

2. The editor of the Central College yearbook is considering having the book printed on a heavier paper stock. Conversations with the publisher reveal that this would increase the cost per book by $.75. What effect would this have on the break-even volume? How much would the price need to be increased in order to keep the same break-even volume that was found in problem 1?

Solution

We first find the break-even volume using the $.75 increase in variable costs.

$$v = \frac{c_f}{p - c_v}$$

$$= \frac{20,000}{12-3.75} = \frac{20,000}{8.25} = 2,424.2$$

The new break-even volume is 2,425.
    Next, we need to see how varying the variable cost and keeping fixed cost and break-even volume constant at their original values will affect the selling price. Using the same formula

$$v = \frac{c_f}{p - c_v}$$

$$2,223 = \frac{20,000}{p-3.75}$$

$$p = \frac{20,000}{2,223} + 3.75$$

$$= 9 + 3.75 = 12.75$$

So the price increase is the exact amount to cover the cost increase.

23 Problem Analysis with Calculus

Key Concepts

I. Many managerial problems require the solution of a nonlinear relationship by differential calculus.
   A. Because the derivative of a nonlinear function is equal to zero at the maximum and minimum values of the function, setting the derivative equal to zero can allow us to obtain the values of the decision variables.
   B. Many classical management science problems lend themselves to this approach.
      1. Profit analysis models allow the volume of demand to depend on price, so that total profit contains a p^2 term, where p = unit price.
      2. The EOQ formula, found in chapter 18 by equating ordering and carrying cost, may also be found by differentiating the total cost expression with respect to Q.
      3. In the case of inventory analysis when shortages are allowed, to solve for the optimal shortage level and order quantity, it is necessary to use calculus, differentiating the total cost expression with respect to both Q and S, setting these derivatives equal to zero, and then solving them simultaneously for Q^* and S^*.
II. Many of these problems, which have nonlinear profit or cost relationships, also have restrictions on the problem. Together, we have a nonlinear objective function with constraints, or a nonlinear programming problem.

Quiz

True-False

T F   1. The derivative of the functional equation of a curve gives its slope.
T F   2. The maximum slope of a curve occurs at the maximum value of the curve.
T F   3. Solving the differentiated functional equation set equal to zero will give the break-even values in any problem.
T F   4. Differential calculus is not useful when the functional relationship is linear.
T F   5. When demand varies with price, the expression for total profit will be nonlinear.
T F   6. Finding the optimal price in a nonlinear profit problem usually results in calculation of optimal rather than break-even volume.
T F   7. To solve for the EOQ formula using calculus, our goal is to minimize ordering cost.
T F   8. The reason the EOQ formula can be solved without calculus is that the minimum total cost occurs when ordering and carrying costs are both minimized.
T F   9. It is possible to solve for Q^* in the shortage model without solving for S^*.
T F   10. Total cost in the shortage model is located where ordering and carrying cost are equal.

Problems

1. Demand for tickets to a concert is found to decrease as the cost per ticket increases, according to the expression

   demand volume $= 1{,}000 - 50p$

   Most of the costs of the concert are fixed, and the total fixed cost is figured at $3,000. Variable costs, for hall rental and security, are figured at $2.00 per customer.
       How should tickets be priced, what is the optimal volume, and what is the optimal profit?

Solution

The profit expression is given by total revenue minus fixed costs minus variable costs, or

$$Z = (1,000 - 50p)p - 3,000 - (1,000 - 50p)2$$

The derivative of this expression is

$$\frac{dZ}{dp} = -100p + 1,100$$

When set equal to zero, we find

$$p = 11$$

so the optimal price per ticket is $11.00. This gives a volume of

$$(1,000 - 50(11)) = 450$$

and the optimal profit of

$$\begin{aligned} Z &= -50(11)^2 + 1,100(11) - 5,000 \\ &= -6,050 + 12,100 - 5,000 \\ &= \$1,050 \end{aligned}$$

2. Consider an inventory system with the following values for the inventory parameters:

$$C_s = \$1.50 \text{ per unit}$$
$$C_c = \$3.50 \text{ per order}$$
$$D = 2,000 \text{ units per year}$$

Develop the total cost function and determine the optimal order quantity and shortage level.

Solution

Total cost is given by order cost plus inventory carrying cost plus shortage cost according to the formula

$$TC = \frac{C_s S^2}{2Q} + C_c \frac{(Q - S)^2}{2Q} + C_o \frac{D}{Q} \quad (1)$$

Substituting the given values into (1) we have

$$TC = \frac{1.5S^2}{Q} + \frac{1.75 (Q - S)^2}{Q} + \frac{740,000}{Q} \quad (2)$$

Differentiation will be simpler if we first expand terms in (2)

$$TC = \frac{.75S^2}{Q} + 1.75Q - 3.5S + \frac{1.75S^2}{Q} + \frac{740,000}{Q} \quad (3)$$

We must take the partial derivative of TC (3) with respect to both Q and S.

$$\begin{aligned} \frac{\partial TC}{\partial Q} &= \frac{-.75S^2}{Q^2} + 1.75 - \frac{1.75S^2}{Q^2} - \frac{740,000}{Q^2} \\ &= \frac{-2.5S^2}{Q^2} + 1.75 - \frac{740,000}{Q^2} \end{aligned}$$

$$\begin{aligned} \frac{\partial TC}{\partial S} &= \frac{1.5S}{Q} - 3.5 + \frac{3.5S}{Q} \\ &= \frac{5S}{Q} - 3.5 \quad (5) \end{aligned}$$

Equating both partial derivatives (4) and (5) to zero, we see

$$\left(\frac{-2.5S^2}{Q^2}\right) + 1.75 - \frac{740,000}{Q^2} = 0$$

$$-2.5S^2 + 1.75Q^2 = 740,000 \qquad (6)$$

and

$$\frac{5S}{Q} - 3.5 = 0$$

$$S = \frac{3.5Q}{5} = .7Q \qquad (7)$$

Substituting equation (7) into equation (6),

$$-2.5(.7Q)^2 + 1.75Q^2 = 740,000$$
$$.525Q^2 = 740,000$$
$$Q^2 = 1,409,524$$
$$Q^* = 1,187$$
$$S^* = .7(1,187) = 831$$

24 Nonlinear Programming

Key Concepts

I. Nonlinear programming problems are mathematical programming problems with objective functions and/or constraints that are not linear relationships.
  A. The optimization of a nonlinear objective function may be constrained or unconstrained.
    1. Unconstrained optimization problems are often solved by the differentiation techniques of chapter 23.
    2. Constrained optimization is very difficult to solve, but if the constraint is an equality, one of two techniques may be used to "unconstrain" the problem.
      a. The substitution method solves the constraint for one of the decision variables, then substitutes the expression for that variable in the objective function, effectively removing the constraint.
      b. The method of Lagrange multipliers subtracts the product of a coefficient (Lagrange multiplier) and the linear constraint set to zero from the objective function, finds partial derivatives with respect to all decision variables and the Lagrange multiplier, sets them equal to zero, and solves simultaneously for the variables and multiplier.
  B. One of the most difficult aspects of nonlinear programming is that the feasible region will probably be quite irregular in appearance and the optimal solution may very well be in the interior of the feasible region.
II. Many nonlinear programming problems are too complicated for solution without a computer.
  A. Some objective functions contain both concave and convex portions, and so setting the first derivative equal to zero is no guarantee of finding the optimal solution.
  B. Gradient search techniques, conducted on the computer, are systematic ways to search for locally, then globally, optimal points.

Quiz

True-False

T F   1. Math programming problems with either nonlinear objective function or constraints are called nonlinear programming problems.

T F   2. Nonlinear programming problems can be solved by the simplex procedure.

T F   3. It is possible to have an objective to be satisfied that is not subject to any constraints.

T F   4. As in linear programming, the optimal solution to a nonlinear problem will be at an extreme point.

T F   5. The substitution method can be used to convert a constrained optimization problem (with an inequality constraint) to an unconstrained problem.

T F   6. A Lagrange multiplier is used to combine a constraint with the objective function.

Exercises

7. Give the revised objective function for this nonlinear programming problem using the substitution method.

    maximize $Z = 12x_1 - 2x_1^2 + 72 + 5x_2 - .1x_2^2$
    subject to
    $x_1 + x_2 = 6$

8. Solve for the optimal solution in question 7 by differentiating the objective function.

9. Use the method of Lagrange multipliers to revise the objective function in question 7.

10. Using partial derivatives, confirm your answer to question 8 by using the objective function developed in question 9.

Problems

1. A company would like to maximize profit subject to meeting a demand constraint. The relationships are given in the following nonlinear programming problem.

$$\text{maximize } Z = vp - 20,000 - 25v$$
subject to
$$v = 1,000 - 5p$$

Solve this problem using the substitution method.

Solution

Since the constraint has already been written in terms of one of the decision variables, we can easily substitute for v in the objective function. This results in the unconstrained objective function.

$$
\begin{aligned}
Z &= (1,000 - 5p)p - 20,000 - 25(1,000 - 5p) \\
&= 1,000p - 5p^2 - 20,000 - 25,000 + 125p \\
&= -5p^2 + 1,125p - 45,000
\end{aligned}
$$

Next, to find the value for p where Z is maximized, we will differentiate Z with respect to p.

$$\frac{\partial Z}{\partial p} = -10p + 1,125$$

Setting the derivative equal to zero and solving for p we find:

$$
\begin{aligned}
0 &= -10p + 1,125 \\
10p &= 1,125 \\
p &= 112.5
\end{aligned}
$$

and

$$
\begin{aligned}
v &= 1,000 - 5(112.5) \\
v &= 437.5
\end{aligned}
$$

2. Solve the following nonlinear programming problem by the method of Lagrange multipliers.

$$\text{maximize } Z = 3x_1 - .2x_1^2 + 7x_2 - .5x_2^2$$
subject to
$$2x_1 + 3x_2 = 20$$

Solution

The first step is to form the Lagrangian function, L, by transforming the constraint so that it is equal to zero, multiplying the resulting expression by λ, and subtracting that product from the objective function.

$$L = 3x_1 - .2x_1^2 + 7x_2 - .5x_2^2 - \lambda(2x_1 + 3x_2 - 20)$$

The next step is to partially differentiate L with respect to x_1, x_2, and λ.

$$\frac{\partial L}{\partial x_1} = 3 - .4x_1 - 2\lambda$$

$$\frac{\partial L}{\partial x_2} = 7 - x_2 - 3\lambda$$

$$\frac{\partial L}{\partial \lambda} = -2x_1 - 3x_2 + 20$$

The next step is to set each equation equal to zero and solve them simultaneously.

$$3 - .4x_1 - 2\lambda = 0$$
$$7 - x_2 - 3\lambda = 0$$
$$20 - 2x_1 - 3x_2 = 0$$

If we combine the first two equations so that λ can be eliminated, by multiplying the first equation by "-3" and the second by "2" and adding, we have:

$$-9 + 1.2x_1 + 6\lambda = 0$$
$$\underline{14 - 2x_2 - 6\lambda = 0}$$
$$5 + 1.2x_1 - 2x_2 = 0$$

We can then combine this equation with the third to eliminate x_2, by multiplying this equation by "-3" and the third equation by "2" and adding.

$$5 + 1.2x_1 - 2x_2 = 0$$
$$20 - 2x_1 - 3x_2 = 0$$

$$-15 - 3.6x_1 + 6x_2 = 0$$
$$\underline{40 - 4x_1 - 6x_2 = 0}$$
$$25 - 7.6x_1 = 0$$
$$x_1 = 3.29$$

Substituting this value into the previous equations we can find the optimal values for x_2 and λ,

$$5 + 1.2(3.29) - 2x_2 = 0$$
$$5 + 3.95 - 2x_2 = 0$$
$$2x_2 = 8.95$$
$$x_2 = 4.48$$
$$3 - .4(3.29) - 2\lambda = 0$$
$$3 - 1.32 - 2\lambda = 0$$
$$2\lambda = 1.68$$
$$\lambda = .84$$

The value of the objective function is

$$Z = 3(3.29) - .2(3.29)^2 + 7(4.48) - .5(4.48)^2$$
$$= 9.87 - 2.16 + 31.36 - 10.04$$
$$= 29.03$$

The value $\lambda = .84$ means that a change of the right-hand side of the constraint from 20 to 21 would increase the value of the objective function by \$.84, from \$29.03 to \$29.87.

Case *Mrs. Worthington's Portfolio*

"Cheryl, here is the summary I told you about yesterday. I think it should make it fairly easy for you to set up Mrs. Worthington's portfolio, since we're only considering three stocks for her. Once you get all the information on the returns, you can solve the problem and get in touch with her. Let me know how it comes out."

With this introduction, Stephen Scott, the local manager of a large investment house, handed Cheryl Hansen, the office's newest analyst, a copy of the report summarized in exhibit 24.1. Cheryl's first real assignment for the firm was to develop a portfolio for Mrs. George Worthington, a wealthy and very conservative widow. The job, thought Cheryl, should be ridiculously simple since Mrs.

Worthington had decided to consider only EXYCON, CANEX, and CTE corporations in which she had extreme faith.

As Cheryl scanned the summary, she made some notes on what information she would need and concluded that the office's library of annual reports, back issues of the *Wall Street Journal* and *Barron's,* and a good statistics book would help her to calculate the expected returns and covariance of returns. After several hours of work, she had developed the information shown in exhibit 24.2. Her only remaining task was to formulate and solve the non-linear programming problem.

Exhibit 24.1 Summary of Portfolio Analysis Based on Markowitz, *Portfolio Selection*

Corporate Fact Summary 32/8-55

Given a choice between two portfolios with the same expected rate of return, the rational investor will prefer the portfolio with the lower risk. If two portfolios have the same risk, the rational investor will prefer the portfolio with the higher return. Therefore, most investors will prefer a portfolio with high return and low risk. Diversification is one way to reduce risk and possibly increase return.

Risk can be represented by the covariance between securities, and the investor's attitude toward risk should be reflected in the construction of the portfolio. This should be done by weighting the return portion of the objective function with a multiplier m, which is zero or positive. A value of 0 for m means the objective is to minimize risk and completely disregard return. A base value for m for conservative customers might be $m = 1$.

$$\text{minimize } Z = -m \sum_{i=1}^{n} r_i x_i + \sum_{i=1}^{n} \sum_{j=1}^{n} x_i x_j \text{ cov } (r_i/r_j)$$

subject to

$$\sum_{i=1}^{n} x_i = 1$$

where
x_i is the fraction of the portfolio invested in security i
r_i is the expected return for security i

Exhibit 24.2 Returns and Covariances for the Three Stocks

Stock	Expected Return
EXYCON	3.2
CANEX	6.5
CTE	1.8

	Variance-Covariance		
	EXYCON	CANEX	CTE
EXYCON	2.0	4.3	1.2
CANEX	4.3	5.7	2.8
CTE	1.2	2.8	.75

Nonlinear Programming

25 The Manager and Management Science

Management Information Systems and Implementation

Key Concepts

I. Management science techniques do not make decisions but rather provide information that can aid the manager in making decisions.

II. The vehicle for accumulating information for use in management science techniques, executing these techniques, and disseminating this information to management is the *management information system.*

  A. The first stage in a management information system is the development of a *data base,* which is an organized collection of numerical information such as prices, production levels, resources, capacities, and rates.

    1. The information contained in the data base must be relevant, accurate, and adequate.

    2. The volume and complexity of the information almost always requires the use of a computer to keep it all organized.

  B. A computer system not only organizes the information in the data base but also can apply quantitative management science techniques and other analysis to the numerical information.

    1. The actual computer and other machines such as printers, keypunch machines, and terminals are called *hardware.*

    2. *Software* describes the mathematical and written codes and the programs that tell the computer what to do, which may be developed by the company using it or be purchased as pre-written software.

    3. The information that comes to the manager from the computer can be general summary reports or the results of management science models.

    4. The manager interacts with the computer by asking *what if?* types of questions, either by rerunning the models with different data or by taking advantage of *interactive* software that allows the user to carry on a dialogue with the computer.

  C. The computer can only provide information for the manager; it is up to the manager to use the information to make the best decisions and make the results an additional part of the data base.

III. The availability of a data base, management science techniques, and solutions does not guarantee that managers will *implement* the information to make good decisions.

  A. Some of the failures to implement early management science solutions were blamed on the training of the users; a bad fit between the real problem, the model, the data, and the solution; and a resistance to new tools.

  B. With increased use of management science, much of the problem was seen to lie in the organizational and political climate for management science within the firm.

  C. Although problems of implementation are specific to each company, there are some general strategies that help to achieve implementation.

    1. Implementation should be considered a continuous, ongoing process to provide feedback and insure that each stage of the modelling process is successful.

    2. A joint effort by the manager and the management scientist to create an atmosphere conducive to change and one in which the manager will be prepared for the entire process will aid implementation.

    3. Management science models and their implementation should be enhanced by a cost/benefit analysis.

Appendix A

```
MPOS VERSION 4.0        NORTHWESTERN UNIVERSITY
        ****************************************
        *                                      *
        *             M P O S                  *
        *          VERSION 4.0                 *
        *                                      *
        * MULTI-PURPOSE OPTIMIZATION SYSTEM *  *
        *                                      *
        ****************************************

***** PROBLEM NUMBER  1 *****
        REGULAR
        COLUMNS 80
        TITLE
        LP PROBLEM FOR MPOS
        VARIABLES
        X1,X2,X3
        MAXIMIZE
        1X1+2X2+4X3
        CONSTRAINTS
   1.   2X1+X2+3X3.LE.12
   2.   4X1+X2+X3.LE.6
        NOSCALE
        PRINT
        RNGOBJ
        RNGRHS
        OPTIMIZE



        MPOS VERSION 4.0        NORTHWESTERN UNIVERSITY

**********************
* PROBLEM NUMBER  1 *
**********************

USING REGULAR
LP PROBLEM FOR MPOS
```

PROBLEM INPUT SUMMARY

CONSTRAINTS		VARIABLES		NON-ZEROS		PARAMETERS		BOUNDS
EQS=	0	INT=	0	NUMBER=	6	TOL= .100E-07		
LES=	2	TOTAL=	3	PERCENT=100.00		EPS=DEFAULT		
GES=	0	NOUB=	0			LIMIT=DEFAULT		
TOTAL=	2	NOLB=	0			RSCALE= .100E+01		

VARIABLE TABLE

```
  1 - X1          2 - X2          3 - X3
        INPUT TRANSLATION TIME =      1820 SECONDS



        MPOS VERSION 4.0        NORTHWESTERN UNIVERSITY

**********************
* PROBLEM NUMBER  1 *
**********************

USING REGULAR
LP PROBLEM FOR MPOS
```

INITIAL TABLEAU

ROW	BASIC	VALUES	(1)	(2)	(3)
1	VAR- 0	12.000	2.0000	1.0000	3.0000
2	VAR- 0	6.0000	4.0000	1.0000	1.0000
3	-Z	0.	1.0000	2.0000	4.0000

```
        MPOS VERSION 4.0        NORTHWESTERN UNIVERSITY

********************
* PROBLEM NUMBER  1 *
********************

USING REGULAR
LP PROBLEM FOR MPOS

ITNO.   1 IN VAR-   3  VAR-   4 TO LOWER BOUND  -ZMIN=        16.000000
ITNO.   2 IN VAR-   2  VAR-   5 TO LOWER BOUND  -ZMIN=        18.000000



        MPOS VERSION 4.0        NORTHWESTERN UNIVERSITY

********************
* PROBLEM NUMBER  1 *
********************

USING REGULAR
LP PROBLEM FOR MPOS

            FINAL TABLEAU

ROW     BASIC   VALUES      (  1)        (  2)        (  3)        (  4)
  1   VAR-   3  3.0000    -1.0000       0.          1.0000       .50000
  2   VAR-   2  3.0000     5.0000       1.0000      0.          -.50000
  3       -Z    18.000     5.0000       0.          0.           1.0000

ROW     BASIC   VALUES      (  5)
  1   VAR-   3  3.0000    -.50000
  2   VAR-   2  3.0000     1.5000
  3       -Z    18.000     1.0000



        MPOS VERSION 4.0        NORTHWESTERN UNIVERSITY

********************
* PROBLEM NUMBER  1 *
********************

USING REGULAR
LP PROBLEM FOR MPOS

                  SUMMARY OF RESULTS

VAR   VAR       ROW  STATUS      ACTIVITY      OPPORTUNITY      LOWER     UPPER
NO   NAME       NO               LEVEL         COST             BOUND     BOUND
 1   X1         --    LB       0.0000000      5.0000000        0.0000     INF
 2   X2         --    B        3.0000000      0.0000000        0.0000     INF
 3   X3         --    B        3.0000000      0.0000000        0.0000     INF
 4   SLACK-- D-  1    LB       0.0000000      1.0000000        0.0000     INF
 5   SLACK-- D-  2    LB       0.0000000      1.0000000        0.0000     INF

    MAXIMUM VALUE OF THE OBJECTIVE FUNCTION =        18.000000

    CALCULATION TIME WAS      0110 SECONDS FOR   3 ITERATIONS.
```

Appendix B

```
        MPOS VERSION 4.0        NORTHWESTERN UNIVERSITY

**********************
* PROBLEM NUMBER  1 *
**********************

USING REGULAR
LP PROBLEM FOR MPOS



                          RNGOBJ
                          ******
              (OPTIMALITY RANGE FOR COST COEFFICIENTS)
                      BASIC VARIABLES ONLY

  CJ    XIN        MIN   CJ       ORIGINAL CJ      MAX   CJ       XIN
                   -------       ------------      -------
                   Z-LOWER            Z            Z-UPPER


  3      4        2.0000          4.0000          6.0000          5
                  12.000          18.000          24.000

  2      5        1.3333          2.0000          4.0000          4
                  16.000          18.000          24.000


        CALCULATION TIME WAS    .044 SECONDS



        MPOS VERSION 4.0        NORTHWESTERN UNIVERSITY

**********************
* PROBLEM NUMBER  1 *
**********************

USING REGULAR
LP PROBLEM FOR MPOS



                          RNGRHS
                          ******
           (OPTIMALITY RANGE FOR RIGHT-HAND-SIDE CONSTANTS)
                      NON-SLACK RESOURCES ONLY

  BI    XOUT       MIN   BI       ORIGINAL BI      MAX   BI       XOUT
                   -------       ------------      -------
                   Z-LOWER            Z            Z-UPPER


  1      3        6.0000          12.000          18.000          2
                  12.000          18.000          24.000

  2      2        4.0000          6.0000          12.000          3
                  16.000          18.000          24.000


        CALCULATION TIME WAS    042 SECONDS



    DATA STORAGE MEMORY =000444(OCTAL) TOTAL MEMORY = 050000(OCTAL)
TOTAL TIME FOR THIS PROBLEM WAS   .538 SECONDS


  **END OF LISTING**
```

Quiz Solutions

Chapter 1

True-False

1. False
2. True
3. False
4. True
5. False
6. True
7. True
8. False
9. False
10. True
11. False
12. True
13. True

Short Answer

1. Management science

2.
   a. Observe the situation
   b. Define the problem
   c. Construct a model of the problem
   d. Solve the model
   e. Implement the results

Chapter 2

Short Answer

1. Permissible objective functions are a, b, c, f, and g.

2. Permissible constraints are a, c, d, e, f, and h.

3.
   a. $5x_1 + 3x_2 \leq 300$
   b. $4x_1 + 8x_2 \leq 500$
      $\quad\quad 2x_1 \leq 800$
   c. $x_1 + x_2 \leq 75$
   d. $x_1 - 2x_2 \leq 0$

4.
   a. Infeasible because $3(8) + 4(6) = 48$, violating the first constraint.
   b. Infeasible because $3(2) + 4(5) = 26$, violating the first constraint.
   c. Feasible
   d. Infeasible because $3(0) + 4(7) = 28$, violating the first constraint.
   e. Infeasible because $2(5) - 1(2) = 8$, violating the third constraint.
   f. Infeasible because $2(4) - 1(3) = 5$, violating the third constraint.

Chapter 3

True-False

1. False
2. True
3. False
4. True
5. False
6. True

Exercises

7. $x_1 = 0, x_2 = 2$
8. $x_1 = 46/5, x_2 = 14/5$
9. $x_1 = 2, x_2 = 2$

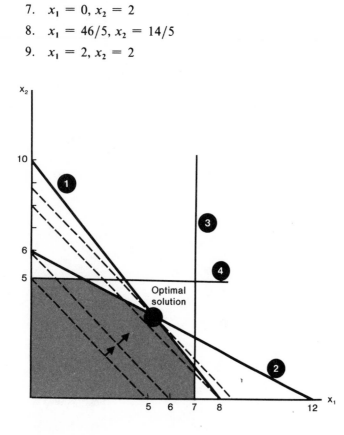

10. See graph.

11. See graph.

12. See graph. Optimal solution is the intersection of 1 and 2.

13. Constraints 1 and 2. Solution is $x_1 = 16/3, x_2 = 10/3$, with objective function value $Z = 26/3$.

14. Solution is the same as question 13 because the slope of the two objective functions is the same.

15. Solution is along the line segment from $x_1 = 2, x_2 = 5$ to $x_1 = 16/3, x_2 = 10/3$ because the objective function has the same slope as constraint 2.

Chapter 4

True-False

1. False
2. True
3. True
4. True
5. False
6.

c_j			10	12	0	0	0
	basic variables	quantity	x_1	x_2	s_1	s_2	s_3
0	s_1	5	1	1	1	0	0
0	s_2	8	2	3	0	1	0
0	s_3	15	4	1	0	0	1
	z_j	0	0	0	0	0	0
	$c_j - z_j$		10	12	0	0	0

7.

c_j			3	7	5	0	0
	basic variables	quantity	x_1	x_2	x_3	s_1	s_2
7	x_2	5	1/2	1	1/4	1/2	0
0	s_2	20	2	0	3/4	$-1/2$	1
	z_j	35	7/2	7	7/4	7/2	0
	$c_j - z_j$		$-1/2$	0	13/4	$-7/2$	0

8. Three decision variables and two constraints.

9. Current solution is $x_1 = 0$, $x_2 = 5$, $x_3 = 0$, $s_1 = 0$, $s_2 = 20$, and $Z = 35$. It is not optimal.

10. x_3 would enter the basis and x_2 would leave.

Chapter 5

Short Answer

1. When there is no initial basis element in a constraint an artificial variable is needed. This usually occurs when the constraint is $\geq$ or $=$.

2. Artificials allow the establishment of an initial basis so simplex can begin.

3. Slack variables are added to the left (smaller) side of $\leq$ constraints in order to create equalities. Surplus variables are subtracted from the left (larger) side of $\geq$ constraints in order to create equalities.

4. M is such a large positive penalty for having an artificial variable in the basis that we would never desire it.

5. The $c_j - z_j$ entry for an artificial variable not in the basis will always be $-M - z_j$, which is always negative since M is very large. Hence the artificial will never re-enter the basis.

6. An artificial variable was added to only one side of an equality, so its only feasible value is 0.

7. In a minimization problem we want to choose the variable that yields the largest net decrease per unit of entering nonbasic variable. By choosing the most positive $z_j - c_j$, we accomplish the same goal as choosing the most negative $c_j - z_j$.

8. The extra zero means that the net effect on the objective function of entering this variable would be 0, so we could have a different solution with the same objective function value.

9. An unbounded solution exists when it is impossible to find the smallest ratio because all denominators are negative or zero. This means the variable that has been chosen to enter could increase without bound.

10. A degenerate solution is one that has a basic variable with a value of 0.

Exercises

11. maximize $Z = 2x_1 + x_2 + 4x_3 + 0s_1 + 0s_2 - MA_1 - MA_2$
subject to
$$x_1 + x_2 + x_3 - s_1 + A_1 = 12$$
$$-x_1 + x_2 + s_2 = 1$$
$$2x_1 + 3x_2 - 2x_3 + A_2 = 30$$
$$x_1, x_2, x_3, s_1, s_2, A_1, A_2, \geqslant 0$$

12. minimize $Z = x_1 + 6x_2 + 3x_3 + x_4 + 0s_1 + 0s_2 + MA_1 + MA_2 + MA_3$
subject to
$$x_1 + x_2 + x_3 + x_4 - s_1 + A_1 = 50$$
$$2x_1 + .5x_2 + x_3 + 1.5x_4 - s_2 + A_2 = 100$$
$$x_1 - x_3 + A_3 = 0$$
$$x_1, x_2, x_3, x_4, s_1, s_2, A_1, A_2, A_3 \geqslant 0$$

Chapter 6

True-False

1. True
2. False
3. True
4. True
5. False
6. True
7. False

Exercises

8. Dual Problem

   minimize $Z = 26y_1 + 18y_2$
   subject to
   $$2y_1 + y_2 \geqslant 1$$
   $$-3y_1 + y_2 \geqslant 6$$
   $$y_1 + y_2 \geqslant 4$$
   $$y_1, y_2 \geqslant 0$$

9. Dual Problem

   maximize $Z = 100y_1 + 0y_2 + 500y_3$
   subject to
   $$y_1 + 2y_2 + 4y_3 \leqslant 14$$
   $$y_1 - y_2 + 6y_3 \leqslant 12$$
   $$y_1, y_2, y_3 \geqslant 0$$

10. $-1 \leq \Delta \leq 3$

11. $15 \leq c_1 \leq 19$

12. $-15/2 \leq \Delta \leq 12$

13. $12.5 \le b_1 \le 32$

14. $x_1 = 10 + (-4)/2 = 10 - 2 = 8$
    $x_2 = 6 - (-4)/2 = 6 + 2 = 8$
    $x_3 = 15 + 2(-4) = 15 - 8 = 7$

Chapter 7

True-False

1. False
2. True
3. True
4. True
5. True
6. True

Short Answer

7. Unacceptable routes are assigned a large positive cost of m.

8. Unacceptable assignments are assigned a large positive cost of m.

9. A degenerate solution is handled by artificially designating an empty cell as having a shipment. The cell must be chosen so that it allows completion of the assigning of the u and v values.

10. No, as long as not all routes in a row or column are prohibited.

11. Cost $= 20(5) + 20(8) + 10(7) + 50(5) = 580$.

12. $u_1 = 0$, $u_2 = -1$, $v_A = 5$, $v_B = 8$, $v_C = 6$

13. No, because cell $(1,C)$ has a negative value of $k = 3 - 0 - 6 = -3$.

14. Cell $(1,C)$.

15. *Primal Problem* (Advanced)
    Let x_{ij} = the amount shipped from source i to destination j, where $i = 1$ or 2 and $j = A$, B, or C.

    minimize $Z = 5x_{1A} + 8x_{1B} + 3x_{1C} + 6x_{2A} + 7x_{2B} + 5x_{2C}$
    subject to
    $$\left. \begin{array}{l} x_{1A} + x_{1B} + x_{1C} = 40 \\ x_{2A} + x_{2B} + x_{2C} = 60 \end{array} \right\} \text{Supply}$$
    $$\left. \begin{array}{l} x_{1A} + x_{2A} = 20 \\ x_{1B} + x_{2B} = 30 \\ x_{1C} + x_{2C} = 50 \end{array} \right\} \text{Demand}$$
    all $x \ge 0$

    Dual Problem
    Let the five dual variables be u_1 and u_2, associated with the supply constraints, and v_A, v_B, and v_C, associated with the demand constraints.

    maximize $Z = 40u_1 + 60\,u_2 + 20\,v_A + 30\,v_B + 50\,v_C$
    subject to
    $u_1 + v_A \le 5$
    $u_1 + v_B \le 8$
    $u_1 + v_C \le 3$
    $u_2 + v_A \le 6$
    $u_2 + v_B \le 7$
    $u_2 + v_C \le 5$

    One of the general rules for formulating the dual problem states that if the primal constraint is an equality, then the associated dual variable is unconstrained in sign. This allows negative, zero, or positive dual variables.

Another principle of linear programming, Complementary Slackness, states that when a primal variable is positive (in the basis), the corresponding dual slack variable is zero. Hence, in those cells for which there is a shipment (x is positive), the associated u and v values equal c (the slack is zero).

The final condition for optimality of a transportation solution is that $k = c_{ij} - u_i - v_j \geq 0$, which insures the feasibility of the dual solution.

Chapter 8

Short Answer

1. Total integer problems require all variables to have integer values; mixed integer problems require only specified variables to have integer values; and 0–1 integer models require variables to have only the values of 0 or 1.

2. It may work when the variable values are large, but it is not, in general, a good idea.

3. Complete enumeration is a procedure that lists all possible combinations of values of all variables and evaluates each to see which best accomplishes the objective.

4. Implicit enumeration uses a rational procedure to eliminate many of the suboptimal feasible solutions from consideration.

5. If a problem has no feasible solution, you should branch from the node with the greatest upper bound.

6. Use the variable with the greatest fractional part.

7. An optimal solution exists when there is a feasible solution with the greatest upper bound value of any ending node.

8. New constraints are $x_1 \leq 2$ and $x_1 \geq 3$.

9. New constraints are $x_2 \leq 8$ and $x_2 \geq 9$.

10. The new solution is an upper bound; the existing maximum integer solution is the lower bound.

Chapter 9

True-False

1. True
2. False
3. True
4. False
5. True
6. False
7. True

Short Answer

8. An optimal goal programming solution would satisfy all goals, while a satisfactory solution would satisfy high-priority goals but leave one or more lower priority goals not satisfied.

9. The modified and regular simplex methods are identical except that the modified method determines the pivot column by examining only the coefficients of the highest priority goal not yet satisfied. The regular simplex method would examine all coefficients in the $z_j - P_j$ row.

10. Since goal programming attempts to satisfy goals according to their priority level, two goals of equal priority should be placed at the same priority level. Otherwise the modeler would have to specify one goal as having higher priority when in fact there was no difference between goals.

11. Because nonbusiness organizations often have multiple objectives other than to maximize profit, goal programming can be used to find solutions that meet as many objectives as possible. For a single objective, such as to maximize profit or minimize cost, linear programming may be more suitable.

Chapter 10

Short Answer

1. Deterministic events are ones that you know will happen (demand equals 100 units). Probabilistic events are ones that will happen with a specified likelihood (the chance of rain is 80%).

2. $P(CBS) = 3/12$
   $P(\text{independent}) = 1/12$
   $P(PBS) = 2/12$

3. $P(\text{junior}) = 15/50$

4. (Self-explanatory)

5. No, probability must be between 0 and 1, inclusive.

6. Yes. Yes.

7. $P(A \text{ and } B) = .4 + .2 - .5 = .1$

8. $P(B) = .2$

9. Yes.

10. No. Yes.

11.

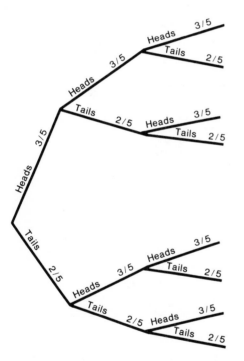

12. From the tree: $P(2 \text{ heads}) = 3(3/5)(3/5)(2/5) = .4320$
    Binomial formula: $P(2 \text{ heads}) = \binom{3}{2}(3/5)^2(2/5)^1 = .4320$

13. $6! = 6 \cdot 5 \cdot 4 \cdot 3 \cdot 2 \cdot 1 = 720$

14. $E(x) = 0(.2) + 1(.1) + 2(.2) + 3(.2) + 4(.3) = 2.3$

15. $\text{Var}(x) = (0 - 2.3)^2(.2) + (1 - 2.3)^2(.1) + (2 - 2.3)^2(.2)$
    $+ (3 - 2.3)^2(.2) + (4 - 2.3)^2(.3) = 2.21$

Chapter 11

Exercises

1. Decision I

2. Decision III

3.

	States of Nature		
	1	2	3
Decisions I	0	3	4
II	7	0	1
III	4	3	0

4. Decisions I and III are tied.

5. If $\alpha = .2$, for example, choose decision III.

6. Decisions I and III are tied.

7. Decision II

8. EOL(decision I) = 2.8, EOL(decision II) = 1.8, EOL(decision III) = 2.

9. Expected value given perfect information is 7.6.

10. EVPI = 1.8

11. Optimal strategy is to choose D_1 with expected value $5,520. If E_1 happens, choose D_3 with expected value $6,400.

12.

Table 11.1 Computation of Posterior Probabilities

States of Nature	Prior Probabilities	Conditional Probabilities	Prior x Conditional	Posterior Probabilities
High	$P(H) = .2$	$P(F \mid H) = .8$	$P(F \text{ and } H) = .16$	$P(H \mid F) = .500$
Medium	$P(M) = .4$	$P(F \mid M) = .3$	$P(F \text{ and } M) = .12$	$P(M \mid F) = .375$
Low	$P(L) = .4$	$P(F \mid L) = .1$	$P(F \text{ and } L) = .04$	$P(L \mid F) = .125$
			$P(F) = .32$	
High	$P(H) = .2$	$P(N \mid H) = .1$	$P(N \text{ and } H) = .02$	$P(H \mid N) = .066$
Medium	$P(M) = .4$	$P(N \mid M) = .5$	$P(N \text{ and } M) = .20$	$P(M \mid N) = .667$
Low	$P(L) = .4$	$P(N \mid L) = .2$	$P(N \text{ and } L) = .08$	$P(L \mid N) = .267$
			$P(N) = .30$	
High	$P(H) = .2$	$P(U \mid H) = .1$	$P(U \text{ and } H) = .02$	$P(H \mid U) = .053$
Medium	$P(M) = .4$	$P(U \mid M) = .2$	$P(U \text{ and } M) = .08$	$P(M \mid U) = .210$
Low	$P(L) = .4$	$P(U \mid L) = .7$	$P(U \text{ and } L) = .28$	$P(L \mid U) = .737$
			$P(U) = .38$	

Chapter 12

True-False

1. True
2. False
3. True
4. False
5. True

Short Answer

6. Dominant strategies guarantee a win. Dominated strategies can be discarded, thus clarifying the choices.

7. A mixed strategy is necessary when there is no equilibrium point.

8. Yes. By knowing what the competitor will do each time, you can protect your own position.

9. More than two strategies mean more than two complementary probabilities to determine, so constraints are needed.

10. The strategy with the highest probability could be chosen, or you could use one of the rules for decision making without probabilities, depending on the importance of the problem.

Chapter 13

True-False

1. False
2. True
3. True
4. False
5. False
6. False
7. True
8. True
9. True
10. True

Exercises

11. No. The entries in row 2 of the matrix do not sum to 1.0, a necessary condition for a transition matrix.

12. The probability of being in state 2 next period given state 1 this period is 0.57. The probability of being in state 2 in the third period given state 1 in the first period is $(.43) (.57) + (.57) (.38) = 0.4617$.

13. Adding the two probabilities marked with an * gives $.2451 + .2166 = 0.4617$, which agrees with question 12.

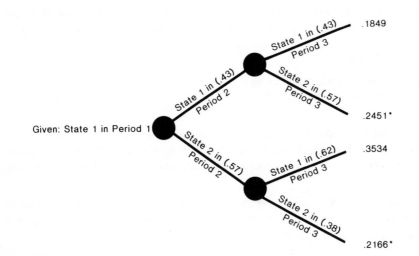

Chapter 14

True-False

1. False
2. True
3. False
4. True
5. True
6. True

Short Answer

7. The analysis should be performed for each period (say hourly) where the arrival rate is different.

8. (Self-explanatory)

9. Unfortunately, waiting lines don't always reach steady-state due to rapidly changing conditions or operation of the system for insufficient time. Also, beginning and ending conditions may be important to study and steady-state characteristics don't reflect those situations.

10. The two-channel system will always provide lower average customer waiting times than the one-channel system, provided they both have the same utilization.

Chapter 15

True-False

1. False
2. True
3. False
4. True
5. False
6. True
7. True
8. False
9. False
10. False

Short Answer

11. If either model is improperly designed and validated, or if only a few simulation trials are obtained, we would not expect the simulation and theoretical results to agree.

12. Financial applications include capital budgeting and cash flow problems, financial planning, rate of return calculations, portfolio evaluations, and foreign currency exchange policies. Marketing applications of simulation include new product introductions, promotion strategy, advertising effectiveness, product pricing and market share analysis, and distribution channel studies.

13. By systematically varying the input (decision) variables and using the simulation model to measure the system's response to these inputs, one can "zero in" on the optimal choices for the decision variables. This is called a search technique.

14. Starting and ending conditions can affect the system's operating characteristics, particularly if steady-state conditions are not maintained by the system. Frequently we are interested in startup and shutdown behavior of the waiting line system. Most of the problems in this chapter assume that the system is empty at startup time and ignore closing time events.

15. Computers cannot easily duplicate truly random physical events and must use mathematical processes to generate pseudo-random numbers. But the mathematical process can be used to generate the same sequence of random numbers that is useful for duplicating and validating simulation experiments.

Chapter 16

True-False

1. True
2. True
3. True
4. False
5. True
6. True

7. False
8. False
9. False
10. True
11. True
12. True

Short Answer

13. A time-series model uses *only* the past history of the forecast itself while a causal method uses other explanatory variables to prepare new forecasts. Many causal models will include a time-series term as one of the independent variables in order to provide better forecasts.

14. Systematically vary α and use the exponential smoothing model to prepare forecasts for the same time periods. Calculate the forecast errors and find the mean absolute deviation (MAD) for each value of α. Choose the value of α that minimizes MAD.

15. Long-range forecasting is particularly difficult since there is insufficient useful historical data. The technological, economic, political, and social factors that affect the future are so diverse and complex that historical data is of little use for the future. However, long-range plans by organizations represent some of their most important decisions.

16. In general, a higher r^2 means less forecast error for causal models. Conversely, a lower MAD means less forecast error for time-series and causal models.

Chapter 17

True-False

1. True
2. False
3. True
4. True
5. False
6. True
7. False
8. False
9. True
10. False
11. True
12. True
13. False
14. False
15. False

Short Answer

16. a. Carrying cost
    b. Ordering cost
    c. Carrying cost
    d. Carrying cost
    e. Ordering cost
    f. Ordering cost or neither
    g. Neither or carrying cost
    h. Neither

17. If lots are purchased, the order arrives at one time and the inventory is instantaneously replenished. If lots are produced at a gradual rate, the inventory is replenished at a gradual rate.

18. (Self-explanatory)

19. C_s is the cost of stocking out of one unit. S is the maximum shortage level. t_1 and t_2 are times (in years) that inventory and stockouts exist, respectively, during one order cycle.

Chapter 18

True-False

1. False
2. True
3. False
4. False
5. True
6. False
7. True
8. False
9. True
10. False
11. True

Short Answer

12. Q is the order quantity, R is the reorder point, and S_s is the safety stock quantity. $R = S_s + $ expected demand during lead time.

13. The cost of carrying safety stock must be weighed against the cost of lost sales and bad will if stockouts occur. However, no amount of safety stock can completely prevent stockouts.

14. Computer simulation is useful with probabilistic demand and uncertain lead times, especially when a number of inventory policies are to be evaluated.

15. Just as we used $Z\sigma$ to represent safety stock under the normal distribution assumption, we would need to determine the proper "Z" corresponding to the Poisson probability distribution. The standard deviation of demand during lead time (σ) under the Poisson distribution is equal to the square root of mean demand during lead time.

Chapter 19

True-False

1. False
2. True
3. True
4. False
5. False
6. True
7. False
8. True
9. True
10. True

Short Answer

11. The major difference between these procedures is that the former finds the shortest path from the origin to each of the other nodes while the latter finds the shortest paths connecting (spanning) all nodes with at least one other node, not necessarily the origin node.

12. Network flow models are relatively easy to solve and many non-network management science problems can be restated in a network flow structure. The pictorial means of representing such complex problems can provide additional perspective to the manager.

13. Net flow along a branch is calculated by adding all the flows along the branch and subtracting all the flows moving in the opposite direction along the branch. Net flow cannot exceed the directed flow capacities of the branch.

14. If two nodes tie at step 4 in the shortest path problem, both nodes should be added to the permanent set at the same time. Then the algorithm should continue. Ties in step 4 of the minimal spanning tree problem make no difference to the final solution—arbitrarily choose either one and continue the algorithm. Ties may indicate the existence of alternative optimal solutions.

Chapter 20

True-False

1. False
2. True
3. False
4. False
5. True
6. False
7. True
8. True
9. True
10. False
11. False
12. True

Short Answer

13. CPM and PERT differ mainly in their treatment of activity duration—CPM assumes a single, constant time estimate and PERT uses optimistic, most likely, pessimistic time estimates. CPM provides a deterministic critical path and PERT gives probabilistic project time information.

14. In CPM, the nodes represent the activities and the branches denote precedence, with the arrow pointing towards the activity that must follow.

15. No. We assume the critical path activities have no slack. For the final node in the project, LT equals ET.

16. Both CPM and PERT will show the manager which activities are critical and how long the project will take to complete. The manager will know which activities have slack and the latest time he or she can start each activity. The CPM or PERT information can help the manager decide which activities to expedite in order to change the project's completion time.

17. Shared slack is the slack that is shared with other activities. The sum of the delays for all activities sharing the same slack cannot exceed the shared slack.

18. No. Only errors in the forward or backward passes could cause such a condition, unless the LT for the last node in the project was set at a figure less than its ET. In this latter case, the critical path activities would have negative slack.

Chapter 21

True-False

1. True
2. False
3. False
4. True
5. True
6. True

Short Answer

7. Both of these solution approaches are not rigidly defined. The analyst must completely define and structure the problem before these approaches can be applied. Each application must be completely tailored to the problem at hand. Other solution techniques provide a rigid framework for solving each problem the same way.

8. The stages in this dynamic programming problem are the three different kinds of items that can be packed in the knapsack. The states now are the number of pounds left to be filled *and* the number of cubic feet (or other volume measure) left to be filled. The decisions are the number of items of the given kind to be filled. The returns are the profits resulting in packing the given mix of items. Only the states are different from the textbook example.

9. We would end up with the same (optimal) solution, regardless of the starting state in the salesforce example.

Chapter 22

True-False

1. False
2. True
3. False
4. False
5. False

Exercises

6. Break-even volume is 107 units.

7. Break-even dollar volume is $535.

8. Break-even volume as a percentage of total capacity is 71%.

9. Break-even volume is 136 units.

10. Break-even volume is 128 units.

Chapter 23

True-False

1. True
2. False
3. True
4. True
5. True
6. True
7. False
8. False
9. False
10. False

Chapter 24

True-False

1. True
2. False
3. True
4. False
5. False
6. True

Exercises

7. maximize $Z = 72 + 17x_2 - 2.1x_2^2$

   or

   maximize $Z = 98.4 + 8.2x_1 - 2.1x_1^2$

8. $\dfrac{\partial Z}{\partial x_2} = 17 - 4.2x_2 = 0$

   so $\quad x_2 = 4.0476$
   and $\quad x_1 = 1.9524$

   or

   $\dfrac{\partial Z}{\partial x_1} = 8.2 - 4.2x_1 = 0$

   so $\quad x_1 = 1.9524$
   and $\quad x_2 = 4.0476$

9. maximize $Z = 12x_1 - 2x_1^2 + 72 + 5x_2 - .1x_2^2 - \lambda(x_1 + x_2 - 6)$

10. $\dfrac{\partial Z}{\partial x_1} = 12 - 4x_1 - \lambda = 0$

    $\dfrac{\partial Z}{\partial x_1} = 5 - .2x_2 - \lambda = 0$

    $\dfrac{\partial Z}{\partial x_1} = -x_1 - x_2 + 6 = 0$

    After solving simultaneous equations,
    $x_2 = 4.0476$, $x_1 = 1.9524$, $\lambda = 4.1904$.